THE AC ELECTRIC LOCOMOTIVES
OF BRITISH RAIL

by Brian Webb & John Duncan

DAVID & CHARLES
NEWTON ABBOT   LONDON
NORTH POMFRET (VT)

David & Charles Locomotive Studies

Published titles still in print

The Steam Locomotives of Eastern Europe, by A. E. Durrant

Steam Locomotives of the East African Railways, by R. Ramaer

The British Internal-Combustion Locomotive: 1894–1940, by Brian Webb

Diesel-hydraulic Locomotives of the Western Region, by Brian Reed

English Electric Main Line Diesel Locomotives of BR, by Brian Webb

The Drummond Greyhounds of the LSWR, by D. L. Bradley

Stanier 4-6-0s of the LMS, by J. W. P. Rowledge and Brian Reed

Sulzer Diesel Locomotives of British Rail, by Brian Webb

Locomotive Monographs

All by O.S. Nock, BSc, CEng, FICE, FIMechE

The GWR Stars, Castles & Kings, Parts 1 & 2

The LNWR Precursor Family

Gresley Pacifics, Parts 1 and 2

The Southern King Arthur Family

The Standard Gauge Great Western 4-4-0s, Vols 1 and 2

The Royal Scots of the LMS

British Library Cataloguing in Publication Data

Webb, Brian
    The AC electric locomotives of British Rail.
    — (David & Charles locomotive studies).
    1. Electric locomotives — Great Britain
    2. British Rail
    I. Title II. Duncan, John
    625.2′63′0941   TF975
    ISBN 0-7153-7663-2

Library of Congress Catalog Card Number 79-51098

Photoset in 10 on 11pt Plantin
by Advertiser Printers (Newton Abbot) Ltd,
Devon
and printed in Great Britain
by
Biddles Ltd, Guildford
for David & Charles (Publishers) Limited
Brunel House   Newton Abbot   Devon

Published in the United States of America
by David & Charles Inc
North Pomfret   Vermont 05053   USA

CONTENTS

INTRODUCTION AND ACKNOWLEDGEMENTS

Electric traction on railways offers considerable savings and advantages on heavily trafficked routes. It is unique in contemporary traction systems, having a static power distribution system which, unlike steam and diesel traction, makes its locomotives entirely dependent on this, so that electric locomotives and electrically-powered train sets do not become haulage units until connected to this power system. Because of this peculiarity, an electric locomotive is really a wheeled sub-station using electricity as a prime-mover to drive itself along. The importance of electric railways able to use power generated by any method, so long as electricity is produced, must soon be realised if the oft-forecast energy crisis of the late 1980s is to be avoided.

This book covers the British Rail AC locomotive fleet up to the beginning of 1979, dealing with design, construction, operation, the major problems and their solutions, over the relatively short duration of their operation, less than 20 years. Chapter 2 sets out in basic terms the technicalities of AC rail traction of BR in an attempt to familiarise the reader with the terminology appearing in subsequent chapters, and similarly the use of annotated photographs throughout the book which, hopefully will do likewise.

The book deals primarily with BR locomotives but the integrated development work stemming from the experience gained by British industry with BR AC locomotives has resulted in thyristor locomotives for use at home and overseas. The valuable experience which has accrued to GEC Traction, the principal British manufacturer of AC locomotives and AC locomotive equipment, from the wide variety of BR AC locomotives supplied by electrical companies now part of GEC Traction, must be virtually unique. Not only has GEC and its constituents supplied electric locomotives for AC railways since 1908, but they also have equipment at work on all the major types of electrification, both AC and DC, throughout the world. The GEC slogan 'World leaders in electric motive power' seems justified in view of this.

Without the wholehearted co-operation and interest shown by British Rail and GEC Traction Ltd, the authors would have found it very hard to undertake the research required for this book. British Rail CM&EE (LM Region), Derby (AC Locomotive section) proved most helpful and provided many useful comments as the book proceeded. GEC Traction Ltd has provided access to its archives, and meetings with key staff who have allowed their experiences to be drawn upon.

The authors wish to record their thanks to Adrian Johnson and David Gradwell of BR LM Region, Derby, and to John Legg, Chairman & Managing Director of GEC Traction Ltd, and in particular his staff, Mike Scott, Assistant Marketing Manager; Roger Bugler, Systems and Administration Manager; Bob Ledger, Chief Engineer, Machine Engineering Dept; Dennis Rawle, Section Leader, Machine Engineering Dept; Ron Jones, Service Dept for their assistance. In addition, GEC staff, Harold Towse and Connie Finnigan, who have helped in many ways throughout visits to the GEC Preston works, are gratefully acknowledged.

Other assistance has come from Viscount Rochdale who played an important role at the start of the research work, Norman B. Gardener, formerly Publicity Manager, GEC Traction, now retired; David Wilkinson, Alex Lamb, and T. A. Stubbs of BR Kingmoor Traction Maintenance Depot.

Photographic and general help has come from BR, GEC Traction, Allan Baker, Norman E. Preedy, Tom Heavyside, and Michael J. Oakley

Finally, the officers and members of the Diesel & Electric Group, the Railway Correspondence & Travel Society, and the Stephenson Locomotive Society are acknowledged. The manuscript was edited and typed by Sandra Tassell, to whom the authors are indebted for her hard work.

Brian Webb
John Duncan

CHAPTER 1

BRITISH WORK IN AC
RAIL TRACTION

The history of electric traction has been covered many times during the last 100 years, in most of its wide applications. In Britain, most electrification in past years used (relatively) low voltage direct current. The high voltage alternating-current (AC) system at industrial frequency has only been a feature of the last two decades. This study thus concentrates on matters concerning British work in AC traction in the last 20 years and looks at the history of AC electrification in Britain and by British manufacturers.

Not usually considered an inhibiting factor in the early adoption of electric traction in the British field was the profusion of electricity supply companies, run both privately and by local authorities, and the fact that their generating capacity and the area they served was far from standardised. In addition, variations in voltages and frequencies supplied by stations to their own respective areas created problems, for it must be noted that at the time no national grid electricity distribution system existed.

By the 1920s the steam locomotive was probably fully developed so in the United Kingdom, with almost inexhaustible coal supplies, it was natural that the electrical engineer, though not the majority of locomotive engineers, was looking to coal to generate electrical energy for use on railways. So far as urban transport was concerned, the early adoption of electricity to power street

The first successful commercial AC locomotives in the world? One of three metre gauge Bo-Bo locomotives with Bagnall-built mechanical parts designed and supplied by the then British Westinghouse Ltd of Trafford Park (later Metropolitan Vickers Ltd) to the Thamshavn-Lokken Railway in Norway. They operated on the 15000V 50-cycle 3-phase/6600V 25-cycle single-phase system, and two survived until 1963, one now preserved.

(Collection of Brian Webb)

COMPARATIVE DIMENSIONS AND EQUIPMENT VARIATIONS FOR AC LOCOMOTIVE CLASSES 81 - 85

Locomotive classification	AL1	*81*	AL2	*82*	AL3	*83*
Main contractor and locomotive builder	AEI (BTH)	BRCW	AEI (MV)	BP	EE	VF
Original loco Numbers	E3001-23 E3301/2		E3046-55		E3024-35 E3303-5	
Weight in working order	80.0T		78.4T		73.0T	
Weight of mech parts minus motors and drives	40.4T		40.7T		36.0T	
Length over buffers	56′6″		56′0″		52′6″	
Height over body	12′4¼″		12′4¼″		12′4¼″	
Width over body	8′8½″		8′9″		8′8½″	
Bogie wheelbase	10′9″		10′0″		10′0″	
Bogie centres	31′6″		30′9″		30′0″	
Total wheelbase	42′3″		40′9″		40′0″	
Wheel diameter	4′0″		4′0″		4′0″	
Bogie type	fabricated steel Alsthom suspension		cast steel with swing link suspension		fabricated steel. Conventional axlebox guides	
Pantograph type	Stone-Faiveley		Stone-Faiveley and AEI		Stone-Faiveley	
Main circuit breaker type	Brown-Boveri		AEI		Brown-Boveri	
Rectifier type	Mercury arc multi anode air cooled		Mercury arc multi anode air cooled		Mercury arc ignitron single anode liquid cooled	
Voltage detection equipment	capacitor divider		potential transformer		capacitor divider	
Main transformer	oil cooled LT tap changer		oil cooled HT tap changer		oil cooled LT tap changer	
Traction motor type	AEI (BTH) 189 6 poles		AEI (BTH) 189Z 6 poles		EE 535A 4 poles	
Traction motor drive type	Alsthom Quill		Alsthom Quill		BB-SLM Spring	
Gear ratios Type A Locos	29:76		29:76		25:76	
Type B Locos	26:83		—		20:76	
Traction motor cooling	1 blower per pair of motors		1 blower per motor		1 blower per pair of motors	
Maximum tractive effort	48000 lbs Type A Locos 60000 lbs Type B Locos		48000 lbs —		40000 lbs Type A Locos 48000 lbs Type B Locos	
Continuous tractive effort full field	20000 lbs Type A Locos 24000 lbs Type B Locos		20000 lbs —		20000 lbs Type A Locos 26500 lbs Type B Locos	
HP. continuous rating	full field 3200 weak field 3200		3320 3310		2940 2950	
Speeds maximum mph	100		100		100	
full field	60		62.3		55	
weak field	71		73		72.6	
Brake equipment make	Westinghouse		Davies & Metcalfe		Davies & Metcalfe	
Main air compressor make	Westinghouse		Worthington Simpson		Worthington Simpson	
Exhauster make	Westinghouse		Worthington Simpson		Reavell	
Battery type and rating	Nife 55 amp/hr		Nife 55 amp/hr		Nife 85 amp/hr	
Battery charging	transductor regulator		ballast resistor		carbon pile regulator	
BR Diagram Nos in 1978	81 aV weight 80T 0C 81 bX weight 78T 3C		82 aX78T 10C		83 aX 75T 4C	

tramway systems and, in London, underground railways, fitted into the existing electricity supply system capability, as did surface electrification of rail services on Tyneside, Merseyside, and in the Manchester and London areas. It was unfortunate that the majority of these systems were developed on the direct-current (DC) system, and used the third-rail contact system. There were exceptions both at home and overseas, for British electrical manufacturers and the railway industry were in at the start of alternating current (AC) rail traction.

An interesting Metropolitan Vickers (MV)

AL4	84	AL5	85	
GEC	NBL	AEI (BTH)	BR	NOTES
E3036-45		E3056-95		E3301—2 built as E3096/7, E3305 as E3100. E3303/4 became E3098/9.
76.5T		80.0T		E3100 76T 1C
39T		40T		
53'6"		56'5"		
12'4 7/16"		12'4¼"		
8'8¼"		8'8¾"		
10'0"		10'9"		
29'6"		31'6"		
40'6"		42'3"		
4'0"		4'0"		
fabricated steel. Conventional axlebox guides		fabricated steel. Alsthom suspension		
Stone-Faiveley		Stone-Faiveley		E3055 AEI pantograph
Brown-Boveri		Brown-Boveri		
Mercury arc exictron single anode liquid cooled		Germanium and silicon semi-conductors, air cooled		E3100 silicon semi-conductor rectifier and transductor control.
potential transformer		capacitor divider		
oil cooled		oil cooled		
HT tap changer		LT tap changer		
GEC WT501 6 pole		AEI (BTH) 189 6 poles		
BB-SLM Spring		Alsthom Quill		
25:74		29:76		Type B Locos converted to Type A. E3100 20: 76 as Type A Loco.
—		—		
fan coupled to twin motor-generator sets		1 blower per pair of motors		
48000 lbs		48000 lbs		E3100 50,000 lbs
—		—		
21000 lbs		20000 lbs		Class AL1 81 Type B Locos actually built from new as Type A Locos.
—		—		
3000		3200		
3080		3200		
100		100		
54		60		
66		71		
Davies & Metcalfe		Westinghouse		E3100 and all class Al5 85 fitted with rheostatic braking also. Now removed from E3100, and not operative on the majority of class 85.
Davies & Metcalfe		Westinghouse		
Westinghouse		Westinghouse		
Nife 85 amp/hr		Nife 55 amp/hr		
carbon pile regulator		transductor regulator		
84 aX 75T 7C		85 aX 81T 3C		

contract of that period was the Midland Railway venture in north-west Lancashire on the Lancaster-Morecambe-Heysham line, only 9½ miles, which opened in 1908. The service was operated by a handful of electric multiple unit trains (EMUs) with overhead wire current collection on the 6600V single-phase system at 25 cycles. As we shall see later, this line became very important in British Rail days.

A much larger AC rail system was the South London electrification of the London, Brighton & South Coast Railway. The LBSCR even in these

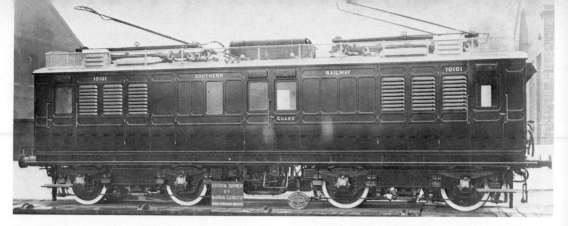

One of the London Brighton & South Coast Railway 1000hp AC power vans built for the South London suburban system. The example illustrated was built by Metropolitan Carriage & Wagon Co Ltd, and had power equipment by GEC. *(GEC Traction)*

early days had seen the advantages of AC over DC electrification, for if its plans to extend this solely suburban network towards the south coast resorts as a main line project materialised, the savings would be great. AC electrification offered cheaper, less complex long-distance feeders compared with DC. AC overhead wire systems required fewer substations with cheaper and simpler switchgear, cabling and so on, not to mention the ease at complex track junctions compared with conductor rail problems at third-rail junctions. It was particularly unfortunate that at the grouping of the UK railways in 1923, the newly-formed Southern Railway decided to adopt for future electrification work, and its ultimate standard, the third-rail DC system. The almost complete adoption of third-rail current collection in the UK was to persist, although there were exceptions, notably the North Eastern Railway (NER) Shildon-Newport mineral line of 1915.

In 1929 a Parliamentary decision eventually led the British electricity generating industry to adopt a standard frequency of 50 cycles per second, but in spite of this the reports of successive committees which studied railway electrification still recommended direct current for UK railways up to 1951. In 1951 the report of the 1927 Pringle committee was finally endorsed, when a committee set up by the British Transport Commission (BTC) and London Transport Executive under Mr C. M. Cock recommended that all future main line electrification should be at 1500V DC with overhead wire current collection. The London & North Eastern Railway (LNER) had already decided to electrify its trans-Pennine Manchester-Sheffield-Wath line, and the Liverpool Street (London)-Shenfield line on this system. Both schemes were postponed during

World War II, but afterwards the BTC authorised completion. Within the next five years a complete reversal of policy on BR took place, so that the 1955 BR modernisation programme authorised all new electrification projects to be carried out on the AC system.

The by now state-owned and unified electricity generating capacity with its national-grid distribution system was seen as a definite advantage by BR, which could take power at 25000V AC 50-cycle industrial frequency and install AC-DC conversion equipment on locomotives and EMUs themselves. This permitted the retention of the well-proven DC traction motor, but at the same time eliminated heavy-current cabling, substations, heavy and complex overhead catenary and supporting structures. There were problems with AC electrification brought about by the restricted British loading gauge.

By this time considerable experience had been gained by BR in AC traction, for the 1951 decision to convert the obsolete and life-expired 1908 Lancaster-Morecambe-Heysham line to 50-cycle 6600V AC had enabled valuation of modern equipment in some refurbished EMUs. Mercury arc, and the world's first traction germanium rectifiers supplied by British industry, together with variations in overhead wire equipment, had proved most valuable since 1953. Similarly, work undertaken in France by the French National Railways (SNCF) on its Aix-les-Bains to La Roche sur Foron line since 1951, and later on the Valenciennes-Thionville line, was proving the 25000V AC 50-cycle system.

Without doubt the decision to go for AC electrification on BR was correct, although in some quarters adherence to the 1500V DC alternative was strong. Had this latter view prevailed BR would have been denied the economics of AC, and on costs alone much of the electrification already done on BR would not have taken place.

CHAPTER 2

THE BASIC PRINCIPLES OF AC ELECTRIC RAILWAY TRACTION

Some readers of this book may be unfamiliar with the terminology and techniques of AC electric traction. It is therefore desirable to deal briefly and simply with some of these at this point.

All forms of matter — gases, solids and liquids — are formed of small particles called atoms. Each atom has an equal number of charged particles called protons (positively charged) and electrons (negatively charged). As the electrons orbit round the atom they are more loosely held than the protons orbiting with the atom. Outside forces such as magnetism produced in a generator, or by chemical action in a battery, can induce the electrons to flow.

Materials like porcelain have their electrons tightly bound together and are called non-conductors of electricity, or insulators. Other materials like copper have loosely-bound electrons and offer little resistance to their flow; these are good conductors of electricity. One cubic centimetre of copper has a vast number of atoms and an even larger number of electrons.

It is the flow of electrons from the terminal of, for example, a battery, where one terminal has an excess of electrons and the other terminal a shortage of electrons, that if both terminals are connected with a copper wire through a load (an electric lamp), the electrons will flow and illuminate the lamp. This would continue until the number of electrons on each terminal was equal and the battery said to be discharged. This flow of electrons is called an electric current. Electricity is known to be present because of its effect as a magnetic force, as heat or light.

A number of common terms are used when dealing with electricity; volts (V) are the unit of electron 'pressure' in a circuit; amps (A) are the amount of electron flow in a circuit; ohms are the amount of resistance to the flow of the electrons. The term watts is calculated by multiplying the volts by the amps in a given circuit, a watt being a unit of electrical power, 746 watts equalling one British horsepower (hp).

BR employs a 25 kilovolts (25kV) system, or

Diagram of the power supply system used by British Rail.

A Heat energy.	**1** Fuel (coal).	**4** 3 phase alternator	**7** BR feeder station.
B Mechanical energy.	**2** Boiler for generating steam.	**5** Step-up transformer.	**8** AC locomotive.
C Electrical energy.	**3** Steam turbine.	**6** Step-down transformer.	*(Brian Webb)*

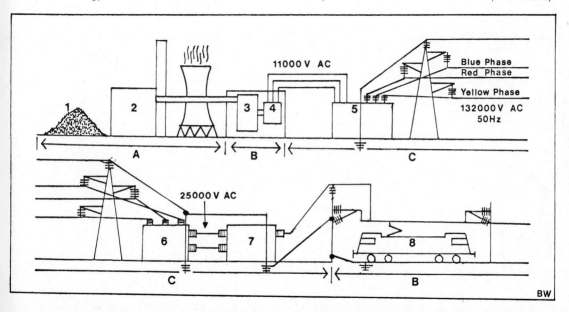

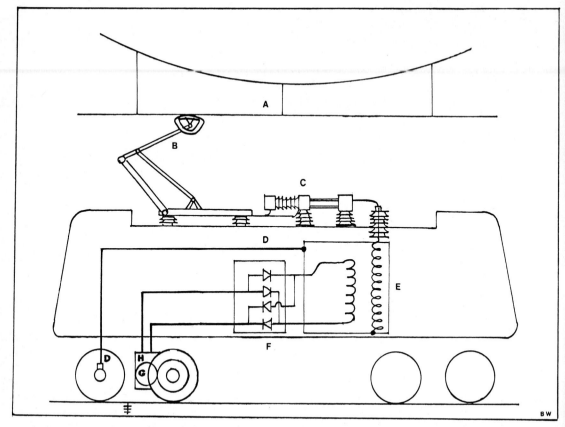

Simplified diagram of BR AC locomotive.

A Overhead contact wire.   **E** Transformer.
B Pantograph.   **F** Rectifier.
C Air blast circuit breaker.   **G** Gearing.   *(Brian Webb)*
D Earth return wire.   **H** Traction motor.

25000 volts. When the term '25kV alternating current (AC), single-phase at 50 cycles per second' is used it is necessary to illustrate this graphically in a simple diagram.

Alternating current changes direction 100 times a second in the British standard system. One complete cycle is 1/50 of a second, so producing 50 cycles in one second. To produce AC the power station employs a steam-turbine to drive an alternator. The alternator rotor is driven by the turbine, the rotor being a rotating electro-magnet which induces an electric current into a stationary coil of wire called the stator. If the rotor rotates at 3000rpm, or 50 times a second, it is single-phase at 50 cycles per second, the British standard. It is normal practice in the UK to use alternators with three phases or three stator windings. The term cycles per second is today usually expressed by the term 'Hertz' (Hz), thus 50 cycles as 50Hz.

Any electric current flowing through a conductor creates its own magnetic field; however, alternating current in doing this has a rising and falling magnetic field because of the current changing direction. If a further conductor is placed adjacent to the conductor with alternating current flowing through it, an alternating current is induced into the second conductor without physical contact. This phenomenon is called the transformer action. It is easy to change voltages up or down without resorting to complex equipment.

Direct current (DC) flows only in one direction in a conductor; it can be produced either in a direct current generator or from a battery, and can also be obtained from AC by passing it through a device called a rectifier. The rectifier is similar in action to a non-return valve in mechanics, for it allows current to pass in one direction only.

AC railway electrification using the overhead contact system at the standard UK industrial frequency of 50Hz was selected for BR. The system has many distinct advantages over DC systems such as that used on BR on the 1500V Manchester-Sheffield-Wath line. Industrial

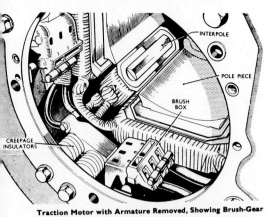

Traction Motor with Armature Removed, Showing Brush-Gear Mounting

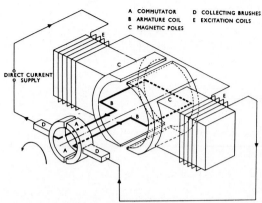

A COMMUTATOR   D COLLECTING BRUSHES
B ARMATURE COIL E EXCITATION COILS
C MAGNETIC POLES

Electric Motor with Series Field System

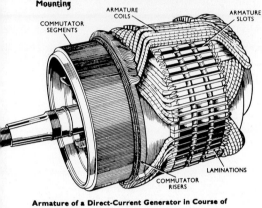

Armature of a Direct-Current Generator in Course of Construction

frequency made it a simple matter to transform the CEGB voltage to 25kV introduced directly into the overhead wires. Fewer feeder stations are required for AC than for DC systems. In the AC system the stations are 30-40 miles apart, and DC four to seven miles apart. The copper contact wire for the overhead wire system is cheaper with AC, being smaller in section and thus less heavy, giving scope for lighter supporting wires and support structures.

So far as locomotives are concerned, a much higher horse-power was conveniently obtainable with AC. A BR class 76 Bo-Bo locomotive running on the 1500V DC system mentioned above has to draw a current of 929A to attain its full 1868bhp. Two class 76 in multiple draw 1858A through four pantographs to produce 3736 bhp. The higher the electric current the bigger the conductors and the heavier the overhead wire. With an AC locomotive on the 25kV 50Hz system, only 100A need be drawn to produce 3300bhp. Two AC locomotives in multiple or tandem, producing 6600bhp with two pantographs raised, only draw a current of 200A, the lower current demand permitting

The electric motor and its components.   (British Rail)

considerably lighter overhead wire and infrastructure costs.

The elimination of steam traction on lines with overhead wire electrification reduced atmospheric pollution on insulators. During the steam era at Crewe on the West Coast main line there were approximately 300 flashovers a year on the AC system overhead insulators to earth; now they are counted in single figures.

An electric locomotive is not 100 percent a true locomotive. Only steam and diesel locomotives can claim this title, as in both instances they produce their own power from coal or oil on the locomotives themselves. An electric locomotive is more a converter of power at the end of a long chain from the power station, via the national grid system, to the railway overhead wires, from which it is collected by the locomotive through a pantograph.

All BR AC locomotives employ DC traction motors. An electric motor converts electrical energy into mechanical energy. The turning force in a motor is done by magnetic force inter-acting with an electric current flowing through the conductors in the rotating part of the motor, or the armature. To understand the DC traction motor it is necessary to discuss the principles of magnetism. Two like magnet-poles, north (N) versus north when placed adjacent to each other produce the invisible lines of a repellent force. Two unlike poles, N versus south (S) give off invisible attracting force lines. An electric current flowing in a conductor (a wire) produces a magnetic field with invisible lines of force.

An electric conductor wound into a coil produces a magnetic field of powerful lines of force, and if the conductor is wound around an iron core, the lines of force become more powerful. If a conductor carrying electric current is positioned between two magnets of unlike poles, it is subjected to a strong mechanical force at right angles to the magnetic field. This forms the basis of the electric motor.

Traction motors are put into reverse by changing the direction of flow of the current flowing through the fixed field coils which surround the moving armature. Reversing the polarity of the electro-magnets in the field coils causes the armature to rotate in the opposite direction.

There are usually four cables to each traction motor. Inside the locomotive body from the transformer, tapchanger, rectifier, and smoothing choke, a flexible cable runs to the motor armature and through this via a flexible return cable to the reversing switch in the locomotive body. A third flexible cable takes the current to the motor field coils, and a fourth flexible cable to the reversing switch inside the locomotive body, and eventually returns to the source of power, the transformer. If the reversing switch throws over, the current changes direction through the field coils only.

Smoothing chokes are fitted to all AC locomotives in the DC circuits after the rectifier. Rectified DC current has what is termed a ripple (peaks and valleys) in its flow pattern. The smoothing choke has little resistance to the DC but the magnetic field produced by its coil 'smooths' the ripple of the AC component by reducing the peaks and raising the valleys. The result is current flow which is acceptable to the DC traction motor. Some heat is produced by the action of the smoothing choke, which necessitates the provision of a cooling fan system.

A DC traction motor armature turns through a magnetic field produced by the fixed electro-magnetic coils around the armature. In doing so it produces its own voltage in the opposite direction to the voltage being applied from the transformer via the rectifiers. As the motor armature increases in speed, the self-generated back-voltage also increases until it almost equals the applied voltage. The problem is overcome by diverting a proportion of the current through resistors in parallel with the field coils. This reduces the magnetic field across the armature and reduces the back-voltage. Thus, more current flows through the armature to increase the speed.

So far as the locomotive driver is concerned, he notices the reading on his notch indicator as it approaches 100 percent tapping from the transformer, and sees that the current being applied to the four traction motors is recorded on the ammeters as falling lower and lower as speed increases. After 100 percent tap, the divert contactors close and the ammeters indicate a rise in traction motor current. The locomotive's speed then further increases and due to increased tractive effort, the current falls again until the second set of divert contactors close; then the current will rise yet again and the locomotive's speed increase further. On some locomotives the range of full power operation can have as many as nine stages of field diversion particularly on diesel-electric locomotives in order to make full use of the limited power of the diesel engine.

The DC series traction motor has a high turning force at starting, rapid acceleration, high turning force with heavy loads and low turning force with light loads, but with high speeds. The AC series traction motor is simpler but is not so good at starting a load from rest. This is because of the fall of the AC voltage from its positive peak, while the AC current continues to rise to peak at its positive value. This is termed lagging. Germany, Switzerland and Austria have AC overhead wire electrification at 15000V with a frequency of $16\frac{2}{3}$Hz — not at the industrial frequency of 50Hz. The lower frequency suits AC series motors and removes the need for rectifiers.

Research work by BR and GEC Traction on the AC three-phase induction motor has resulted in a simple 'squirrel cage' traction motor. It has no insulation on the rotating parts, using air gaps instead, no brushes or commutators, and requires little maintenance. There are disadvantages, as the control and power equipment have to make the three-phase induction motor assume the characteristics of a DC series motor. To do this the AC frequency must be low at starting — 10 cycles — and 100 cycles at speed. On an AC locomotive of this type the 25kV AC single-phase current at 50Hz has to be transformed to around 1400V AC single-phase current at 50Hz, then rectified to DC, and finally inverted back to three-phase alternating current at variable frequency before being used in a traction motor, a complex process. Work in Germany on experimental AC-DC-AC transmissions is being undertaken by Henschel-Brown Boveri, and it is claimed that twice the tractive power is possible at maximum speed from the three-phase induction motor as from the DC

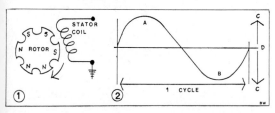

1 Single-phase alternator. **B** North pole passing.
2 Explanation of one cycle. **C** Maximum volts.
A South pole passing. **D** No volts.
One turn of rotor equals one cycle. *(Brian Webb)*

counterpart. On BR the use of thyristor-controlled separately excited DC traction motors, as on 87101 and the Advanced Passenger Train, would seem to indicate a place for the DC traction motor for many years yet. •

All diesel and electric locomotives require auxiliary machines and equipment which are carried on the locomotive. These carry out many services which the locomotive requires and are in addition to the main traction/power equipment.

The AC locomotive requires a source of initial electric power storage in the form of a battery; a means of providing cooling, usually by motor-driven fans which force cool air over heated areas and carry away unwanted heat; a pump to supply oil by a circulating system through radiators cooled by the cooling air, compressed air provided by an air compressor, storage for this air, and electric power for supplying heating or air-conditioning on trains. In fact the auxiliary machines make much of the noise which comes from an electric locomotive. However, the equipment varies greatly, notably in the first four classes of BR locomotive (81-84).

When an electric locomotive is not in contact with the overhead wire the battery is very important. All BR AC locomotives use nickel-cadium batteries which produce 110V DC. This is an alkaline battery, so named because of the type of liquid electrolyte in their cells (potassium hydroxide solution). Diesel locomotives and road vehicles mostly use the cheaper lead-acid battery with a sulphuric acid electrolyte solution.

Nickel-cadium batteries have a long life, robust construction and the capacity to recharge quickly. The battery has 72 cells of approximately 1.5V per cell, connected in series to the output terminals. The battery supplies the lighting, control circuits, auxiliary air compressor motor and (in emergency only) one of the vacuum exhausters. Class 87 locomotives have no exhausters.

The auxiliary compressor runs off the battery

supplying air to raise the pantograph and close the air blast circuit breaker (ABCB) on the locomotive roof, so allowing the pantograph to rise to meet the overhead wire and the circuit breaker to close, thus connecting the main transformer to the power supply. The remaining auxiliaries are fed from the main transformer and are then available for use. The main compressor (all AC locomotives now have the Westinghouse 3VC75 compressor) is motor-driven by taking power from a third or tertiary winding of the main transformer which supplies all auxiliaries. This is AC for AC machines and is rectified to DC for DC machines at 110V, and battery charging on some classes.

Compressed air is available at 140lb/sq in (formerly 100lb/sq in) from the main air reservoirs, these being now located on the locomotive roof at the opposite end to the pantograph in classes 81-85, and slung underneath the locomotive between the bogies in classes 86 and 87. The principal use for the compressed air is to brake the locomotive, and also trains where fitted with air braking. Compressed air is also used for the main power contactors and switches such as the reversers, and power/brake changeover switches. The main compressor also takes over the duties of the auxiliary compressor, operates the locomotive's warning horns, window wipers and washers, and the sanding gear. Classes 81-86 have two vacuum exhausters. Classes 81, 84, 85 have Westinghouse 4V110 piston type units, and the remaining classes the Reavell Fru 5¼X10 rotary type. The vacuum exhauster may be said to be a compressor in reverse, ie it sucks out air, or evacuates the air from the vacuum brake train pipe. BR uses a maximum vacuum of 21in of mercury (21in Hg) which means that the amount of air evacuated from a sealed tube will support a 21in high column of mercury. The most perfect vacuum will support approximately 30in of mercury, or 30in Hg.

The exhausters' motors are supplied by the same system as the main compressor, and by the battery, one off each. The battery-supplied exhauster is used to maintain the vacuum in the train pipe as the locomotive is passing through a neutral section of overhead wire, where the circuit breaker is open, disconnecting the power supply from the transformer.

Tap change motors are small 110V DC units driving the main transformer tap changer, 'tapping-up' to supply more power (volts and amps) to the traction motors, and reversing

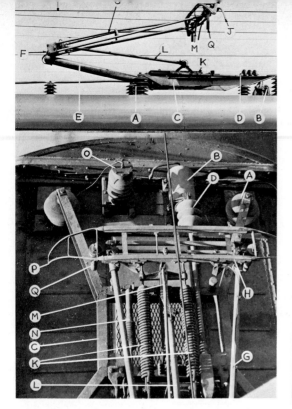

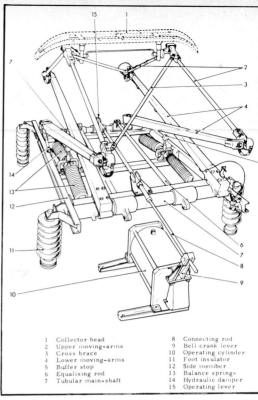

1	Collector head	8	Connecting rod
2	Upper moving-arms	9	Bell crank lever
3	Cross brace	10	Operating cylinder
4	Lower moving-arms	11	Foot insulator
5	Buffer stop	12	Side member
6	Equalising rod	13	Balance springs
7	Tubular main-shaft	14	Hydraulic damper
		15	Operating lever

Above left: BR Stone-Faiveley type AMBR Mk 1 known as the 'bicycle frame' type (upper photo), and type AMBR in lower photo.

A Foot insulators supporting and insulating the pantograph main frame at four corners.

B Pantograph air engine; air pressure allows the control rod (D) to release the pantograph arms and permit the springs (K) to raise the pantograph. Release of air pressure allows springs in air engine to push control rod forward pulling pantograph down.

C Main frame of pantograph.

D Control rod and insulator.   **F** Hinged joint.

E Lower arm assembly.   **G** Upper arm assembly.

H Pantograph head (old type) with eight carbon strips. New type in lower photograph has wire horns.

J Skid bar provided in case of loss of pantograph head. The insulated bar contacts the wire and

interrupts the power supply. This has been replaced by the automatic dropping device (ADD).

K Main springs.

L Thrust rod to position the upper arm assembly correctly in relation to the lower arm.

M Positioning link to maintain pantograph head horizontal at all heights.

N Damper for pantograph main springs.

O ADD insulator showing the air pipe to underside of pantograph head carbons and to the height limit servo valve.

P Pantograph head.

Q Spring plungers to keep pantograph head in contact with the wire.

Above right: Diagram of GEC crossed arm type of pantograph.   *(GEC Traction)*

direction to 'tap-down' and decrease the power to the traction motors. The tap change motor is controlled indirectly by the driver by movement of the main controller handle or 'notching handle'. Class 83 does not have a tap change motor; in its case the tap changer is driven by a three-cylinder radial air motor with oscillating cylinders controlled by electro-pneumatic valves.

On class 85 an auxiliary DC motor, which takes its supply from No 4 traction motor armature during use of the rheostatic/dynamic brake, drives a fan which forces air through the floor of the locomotive and passes via the dynamic braking resistors to be expelled through louvred vent in the locomotive roof, and this air dissipates the heat

energy generated by the resistors. The resistor bank can dissipate 1000kW of electrical power in the form of heat. It was decided that in classes 86 and 87 rheostatic braking would be used over a wider range. This resulted in the need for two sets of braking resistors to absorb a power of 2000kW. Cooling is obtained during braking by a pair of DC motor driven fans.

The ducting to the fan motors incorporates the transformer oil radiators, thus giving the fan motors two cooling jobs to do. Changeover contactors operate when changing from power to braking, changing the power supply to the fan motors from the main transformer to the generated voltage on Nos 2 and 3 traction motors during braking. The remaining auxiliary machines use AC to drive them. The supply comes from the auxiliary winding which is sometimes called the tertiary (third) winding. The machines are all capacitor-start single-phase induction motors, reducing the need for maintenance or carbon brushes and commutators. Class 83 is the only BR AC locomotive with three-phase auxiliaries supplied from an Arno converter.

AC motors carry out a number of functions by driving the following auxiliary machines: cooling fans to cool the traction motors, transformer oil radiators (except classes 86 and 87), rectifiers, smoothing chokes, and also the pump to circulate the cooling and insulating oil from the transformer through the radiators. Classes 86 and 87 have four individual sets of power equipment, each associated with one traction motor. Each power pack group is cooled by one AC fan motor passing air over the smoothing choke, rectifier heat sinks, and the traction motor associated with the power pack. Class 84 is quite different in having two motor generator (MG) sets, each one consisting of a single-phase AC motor driving a DC generator and cooling fan.

The noise levels experienced on AC locomotives when stationary come mainly from the cooling fans. Noise levels are high in classes 81-85 because of the fans' aerodynamic design. Class 86 and 87 noise levels are considerably lower, care having been taken in the design stage to achieve this result. The noise level is less than 96.6 decibels, the acceptable level. By contrast, tests undertaken with a class 83 locomotive at a distance of 5ft 6in above rail level, and 7ft 0in from the locomotive, with all four fans running, put out a recorded noise level of 102.5 decibels. To reduce noise in stations and when standing in built-up areas, the fans stop running when the driver moves the reversing handle to the 'off' position.

BR AC electric locomotives supply electric train heating (ETH) to the coaching stock from the main transformer directly. The supply is nominally 800V AC at 600A maximum load. The supply is connected by contactors which close when a 110V DC circuit is connected correctly throughout the train and locomotive. The locomotive is connected to the train by two large cable jumpers which are pushed into sockets and turned. The turning movement connects the interlocking circuit, and the hinged socket cover latches into the cable end connector. Many of the ETH failures experienced on BR are not due to the power equipment but to the interlocking circuit. If all the cable jumpers between the locomotive and each vehicle are correctly connected, and the driver moves the reversing handle to 'forward' and presses the ETH 'on' button, the ETH contactors close, illuminating the train heating indicator light on the driver's desk. If disconnection of any of the jumper cables occurs, the proving circuit is interrupted and the supply contactors open, causing the indicator light to go out.

Classes 81-85 cannot heat air-conditioned trains as they do not have suitably earthed transformer windings but classes 86 and 87 do. BR diesel locomotives equipped for electric train heating also have the same earth connection linked to their generators.

One aspect not usually given sufficient consideration is the overhead wire and safety associated with AC electrification at high voltages. 'Danger. Overhead Live Wires, 25000 Volts will Kill' really means that if the human body comes in to close contact with live overhead equipment, or with any object hanging from the wires or their support structure, death will result. Rope or string, not normally conductors of low voltage electricity, will conduct 25kV, causing severe burns and death. Railway staff are warned not to approach live overhead wire equipment nearer than 9ft, nor must any object being held do so. On station platforms no part of the human body nor object held by it is allowed above rolling stock cant-rail level on trains standing under the live wire. It is forbidden to cross the front of a locomotive at buffer level, or between carriages or wagons over the top of the buffers. As an added safety guide a one-inch orange line is now being painted at cant-rail level on BR AC locomotives.

These basic rules are needed because 25kV in the overhead wire is just waiting for a conductive object to come near to permit it to flow with great force to the earth, the return circuit to the power station. It is possible for electricity at 25kV to jump across a gap of several inches in the form of an arc to earth through a nearby object that has not actually touched the wire. The only object allowed contact with the wire is the pantograph, so the 9ft ruling must be obeyed to remain alive.

All objects below the overhead wire, including the locomotive and train, are at earth potential to which 25kV is trying to flow, and will if a conductor comes near, and it must be remembered that the overhead wire always looks the same whether live or dead (on or off). Electric current in

Overhead wire structures at Floriston. Single and double cantilever supporting structures in foreground, portal frame type in distance. The earth wire is attached to a small insulator at the top of each structure. The stagger in the overhead is clearly visible, this alternate 8in right and 8in left of track centre allows the contact wire to travel 16in across the pantograph head equalising the wear on the carbon strips. *(John Duncan)*

the overhead wire creates a large magnetic field around the wires and can also induce electric current into objects nearby, for example signal posts, signalbox chimneys, metal footbridges. All these have to be connected by cable to the track, which acts as a return circuit to the feeder station and power station.

When power is first switched on in a new electrification scheme the problems of induction have to be dealt with. An example on the Liverpool-Crewe line was the chimney of Allerton signalbox which became live, the chimney having to be earthed to deal with the problem. In the case of bridges, it was found that by bringing the upper catenary wire nearly parallel to the contact wire, the magnetic field was 'flattened', permitting wire-to-bridge clearance to be reduced from eleven to eight inches, a great saving in bridge construction and reconstruction costs. It is this clearance above and below the contact and catenary wires that adds to the cost of electrification on the overhead wire system because bridges have to be raised or rebuilt to obtain the required clearance, although now less of a problem than an 11in clearance.

The supply at 135kV, or in some cases 275kV,

from the CEGB national grid system is taken at points on the railway where the overhead power lines cross or are adjacent. Two phases are used and transformed to 25kV at each feeder station, usually 30 to 40 miles apart. The two phases are kept separate, one feeding the overhead wire in one direction, and one in the other. Every three to seven miles a track section cabin allows the overhead wire to be isolated into small sections for emergency and maintenance purposes. At 15- to 20-mile intervals are located mid-point track section cabins (MPTSC). These separate the two phases from each feeder section. In the event of failure of one supply at one side of the MPTSC, the other supply can be switched across.

At the feeder station and mid-point track section cabins are neutral sections in the overhead wire. The wire must be structurally continuous, but the two supplies must be kept separate. This is achieved by fitting glass-fibre rods covered with ceramic beads each side of an earth section of wire — the neutral section being 15ft 0in long. As a train approaches the neutral section the driver moves the master controller to the 'off' position, and the air-blast circuit breaker opens to disconnect the supply to the locomotive transformer. This is done by two permanent south-pole track magnets set each side of the track 40-100ft away from the neutral section, two further magnets reconnecting the breaker 40ft beyond the neutral section. The track magnets activate a magnetic switch mounted on the locomotive bogie; this safety device is

Neutral section at the mid-point track section cabin (TSC) on the freight line at Carlisle Upperby, mid-way between Penrith and Kirkpatrick feeder stations.

A Supply cable to mid-point TSC. Vacuum circuit-breakers (VCB) only concerned with the supply from Penrith.
B Supply cable to mid-point TSC. VCB only concerned with the supply from Kirkpatrick, other than in emergency.

C Earthed contact wire between two ceramic bead insulating rods. These separate the north power supply from the south power supply.
D Trackside permanent magnets (TPM) beyond the neutral section (NS) to set the locomotive air-blast circuit breaker (ABCB) thus reconnecting the locomotive to the power supply.
E TPM in advance of the NS to trip the locomotive ABCB and disconnect power supply from the locomotive. *(John Duncan)*

known as Automatic Power Control (APC). If the power were not shut off on the locomotive an arc would be drawn across the neutral section, resulting in a flashover to earth and the supply circuit breakers being tripped out. On the extension of the LMR West Coast Main Line electrification north of Crewe, electric supply to the overhead wire is controlled by Crewe electric control room as far north as Tebay. North of Tebay and on to Glasgow the Scottish control room at Cathcart is in charge. The turn of a switch at Cathcart can, for example, close a circuit breaker over 115 miles south, at Penrith. The control rooms have illuminated panels which show faults, allowing them to be swiftly cleared.

The overhead wire was developed, in design and cost reduction, as the LMR AC electrification was extended, up to 29 percent savings being achieved. Among problems were insulator failures at neutral section, and on the Crewe-Glasgow section with the simple sagged catenary, sections of wire were brought down by high winds. In 1974/5 pantograph blow-offs in the Lake District area

due to high wind velocities caused the overhead wire to billow out and the locomotive to rock. The combination of these resulted in the pantograph leaving the wires at one side allowing it to rise and strike the droppers and pull the wires down, causing much disruption to traffic. The problem was corrected by increasing wire tension, which also improved current collection and reduced arcing. Arcing was common at lower speeds on the later design of overhead wire. With double-headed freight trains before the availability of more locomotives fitted for multiple operation, many complaints were reported by the crews of the trailing locomotives about eye strain at night, because of arcing caused by the leading locomotives.

Arcing damaged pantographs and the overhead wire, in some cases causing locomotive failures by damaging the pantograph dropping device. This device automatically dropped the pantograph if its carbons were damaged, preventing damage to the overhead wire, and also provided identification of points where such damage took place.

CHAPTER 3

E2001 — BRITISH RAILWAY'S
FIRST AC LOCOMOTIVE

It is often overlooked that the first AC electric locomotive to be put to work on BR was not E3001 in December 1959, but E2001 in the autumn of 1958.

With the likelihood of slow and delayed delivery of the various batches of new AC locomotives, steps were taken to provide a locomotive for driver training and testing purposes. The locomotive selected was one of the two Western Region gas turbine machines ordered by the Great Western Railway in 1946 when Swindon, in its usual independent way, chose to experiment with main line gas turbine traction, instead of diesel-electric locomotives then being looked at by its three other compatriot railways in the UK.

Of the two gas turbine locomotives, No 18100 was built by Metropolitan Vickers Electrical Co Ltd at its Trafford Park works under Swindon Lot No 388 in April 1952. 18100 spent considerable periods out of use and at the time of its planned conversion had lain at Dukinfield, Manchester, for a long time. It was officially withdrawn on 1 January 1958, and was towed away for conversion into an AC electric locomotive on 21 January 1958. It went to the Stockton-on-Tees works of Metropolitan Vickers — Beyer Peacock Ltd for this work to be carried out, reappearing still as 18100 and in its black-and-silver livery on 11 October 1958, being towed away the following day. It was allocated to the LMR and was soon renumbered E1000, and again E2001 in October 1959 on the LMR. It usually rejoiced in the nickname of 'Black Bess' and was to retain the livery throughout its life.

Its conversion from a 130-ton gas turbine of Co-Co axle layout to a 105-ton A1A-A1A AC electric locomotive involved considerable alterations to the equipment, the main one being the removal of the gas turbine unit and combustion chambers with its associated DC electric generating equipment, air-filtering units, fuel tanks and control gear. The driving cabs had to be converted from the WR right-hand drive to standard left-hand drive, while the locomotive roof had to be lowered between the cabs to provide a well for fitting of the two pantographs and other roof equipment within the loading gauge. The overall width of the locomotive had to be reduced, so the bogie springing was modified and the large round buffer heads trimmed at their outer edges. Driving cab alterations were done in conformity with the cab layouts adopted for the BR AC locomotives and all instrumentation redesigned. Davies & Metcalfe brake valves were fitted, in addition to the driver's safety device (DSD), and automatic warning system (AWS).

The mechanical portion required little attention and was in good condition. The superstructure was largely welded, having been based upon two main solebars which were continuous plates of deep section with flanges top and bottom for reinforcement, headstocks at the ends tying them together. The main supporting structure was bolted to solebars at each bogie position. In other areas cross-bracing by a lattice of rolled-steel units was used and the whole then topped by a floor-plate. At cant-rail level a ribbed curved plate-section of the roof formed a rigid boom between the cabs, the body sheets being welded to this, to the solebars and carlines; spaces were left to accommodate the louvres. The roof itself was largely of removable aluminium hatches. The cabs were of aluminium construction mounted on the floor plate on top of the frame members.

The bogies were originally built under subcontract at Sheffield by the Yorkshire Engine Co Ltd. These massive units were welded assemblies built up from steel plate and flanges. The side frames were connected by cross-stays and headstocks, stress-relieved by annealing. Body suspension was by eight swing-links, two on each side of the bogie, as in MV standard practice. Metalistic rubber universal joints were fitted, the lower joint was attached to the lower end of the body support brackets, the upper joints to longitudinal equalising beams. In the centre of each beam was a rubber universal joint resting in the corresponding bogie support bracket.

Four out of the original six MV type 271 DC traction motors were retained. These separately ventilated four-pole machines were axle-hung and

The first AC electric locomotive for British Railways.
This was converted from the Western Region gas
turbine locomotive 18100 in 1958, and subsequently
renumbered E1000. In 1959 it became E2001. It was
used for a short period as a training locomotive prior to
the delivery of the new locomotives.   *(GEC Traction)*

nose-suspended. Their continuous rating was
550A, 660V at 706rpm/33½mph, and their one-
hour rating 650A, 565V at 580rpm/27½mph.
They took a maximum current of 1100A, and
voltage 825. Single-reduction gearing with a ratio
of 21:58 was fitted.

New equipment necessary to its conversion
included Stone-Faiveley pantographs, a Brown-
Boveri 22.5kV 360A air-blast circuit breaker, and
main mercury arc rectifiers. The remainder of the
equipment was by MV and included voltage
transformer, main transformer, auxiliary rectifier,
smoothing chokes, AC cooling fans for main
rectifier and smoothing choke.

Certain original items were retained — Keith-
Blackman traction motor blowers, Westinghouse
vacuum exhausters and main air compressor,
radiator and cooling fan, and the batteries.

The body interior layout provided a small
messroom behind No 1 end cab, which
accommodated drivers awaiting their turn for
instruction, and the equipment was laid out to give
inter-cab access through the locomotive body.
The transformer was situated in the middle of the
body with the main rectifier on one side and the
transformer cooling radiators and chokes at the
other. The main transformer consisted of two
units in one tank, an auto-transformer with 38 taps
feeding a main step-down transformer supplying
the main rectifiers. Electric train heating was
provided by an 800V tapping into the auto-
transformer and a 240V tapping to supply the
auxiliary motors and auxiliary transformer.

The Hackbridge & Hewittic mercury arc
rectifiers consisted of 16 four-anode glass bulbs
connected in bi-phase to provide the supply to the
traction motors, the normal load being distributed
between the bulbs by anode compensators. DC
excitation gave stability with the voltage variations
found in traction. Continuous rating of the
rectifier was 2800A at 975V; each bulb was fan-
cooled. The whole of the rectifier was inside a
compartment heated by electricity in cold
weather, the ventilating air coming from a Keith-
Blackman fan which took in air through Vokes
bodyside filters. Between each traction motor and
the main rectifier an iron-cored smoothing choke
was fitted to limit the amount of ripple in the
current delivered to the motor; the chokes were
air-blast cooled.

The oil-filled, naturally cooled, underframe-
mounted 65kW auxiliary transformer had a
bridge-connected germanium rectifier unit which
fed 110V DC to auxiliary motors, control circuits,
lighting, and battery charging, the rectifiers being
side-by-side and air-cooled. The control
equipment operated at 110V DC or, in the case of
pneumatic equipment, 70lb/sq in.

A system was fitted which allowed the batteries
to feed the traction motors and so move the
locomotive when not able to obtain power from the
overhead wire, or when remote from it. E2001 cab
controls included a master controller with two
mechanical-interlocked handles. The reverser
handle selected *reverse, forward,* or *off,* and the
other — the power handle — had six positions, *off,*

run-back, notch-back, hold, notch-up, and run-up, to control power to the traction motors from the tap-changing equipment. The run-up position could only be selected against a spring action which returned the handle to notch-up.

E2001 was put to work on the first electrified section of the Manchester-Crewe lines (the Styal line between Mauldeth Road and Wilmslow) in the late autumn of 1958, along with some electric multiple units intended for the Tilbury line electrification but lent to the LMR until its own train sets were delivered.

Crew training was the job of the EMUs and E2001, the latter being the only AC locomotive available on BR for over 12 months, due to delayed deliveries of new locomotives. E2001 was stabled and maintained at East Didsbury, but was allocated to Manchester Longsight depot.

As deliveries of AC locomotives proceeded, E2001 visited a number of places for instruction purposes, spending time at Liverpool (Allerton) depot and Crewe depot. In April 1961 it was despatched to Glasgow for testing purposes on the Glasgow suburban AC system. Subsequently, after return south, it was less used and was virtually stored at Crewe, Goostrey and Rugby for periods, with brief uses for instructional purposes. It was withdrawn in 1968 but survived until mid-1972, stored near Market Harborough, and finally in Rugby EMU sidings. E2001 was sold to John Cashmore Ltd of Tipton on 15 September 1972 for scrap.

CHAPTER 4

THE FIRST AC LOCOMOTIVE ORDERS

When the implications of the 1955 modernisation programme were made public, it was at this point that all new electrification on BR was standardised on the industrial frequency AC system. The exception was the Southern Region third-rail DC system which was to be expanded, for obvious reasons, in the same way.

Initially, it was the intention to use the AC system on some 1200 miles of BR routes, Euston-Crewe-Manchester-Liverpool; King's Cross-Leeds-York; Liverpool Street-Ipswich, and branches to Clacton, Harwich, and Felixstowe. In addition, suburban lines out of King's Cross and Moorgate to Hitchin and Letchworth; the London-Tilbury-Southend line, and the Enfield, Chingford, Hertford, Bishop's Stortford lines out of Liverpool Street. In Scotland, the Glasgow suburban lines were included. Much of this was carried out, although new schemes replaced some of the original ones.

The London Midland Region (LMR) West Coast Main Line (WCML) from Euston to Manchester and Liverpool was the prototype scheme authorised. So far as rolling stock was concerned, multiple-units were proposed for some services, but the proposed mixed-traffic locomotives were to be standardised in a number of aspects, especially in driving technique and cab control layout. This was in complete contrast to the diesel locomotive designs which were based on so brief a specification that each manufacturer was virtually left to 'do his own thing'.

Electric locomotives have advantages over diesel locomotives in that they are able to draw on very large amounts of power from the supply system, not being restricted by their physical size. The tractive effort of the electric locomotive is only limited by its wheel-rail adhesion over most of the speed range and by the maximum permissible drawbar capacity of the train which it is hauling.

It was initially decided that the British loading gauge and specified electrical clearances necessitated a two-voltage overhead wire supply system to negotiate tunnels and overbridges which could not for practical or financial reasons be rebuilt, or alternatively the trackbed lowered, to gain sufficient clearance for the wires. A reduced voltage of a quarter of 25kV — or 6.25kV — was selected for restricted heights. This made it necessary to have voltage detection and changeover equipment on the multiple-units and locomotives.

Sections of the overhead wire energised at different voltages or supplied from different feeder stations were separated by neutral sections. Although the pantograph ran along a continuous wire system, each neutral section consisted of two insulated runners with an earthed conductor between these insulators. A receiver mounted on the vehicle was to detect a trackside magnet on the approach to a neutral section which cut off and locked out the power circuits by electrical relay interlocking. The circuits were released by a second magnet after the neutral section which restored the power supply to the vehicle.

The West Coast Main Line south of Liverpool and Manchester, and the Eastern & North Eastern Regions East Coast Main Lines, were fairly level in character, and the initial locomotives were designed especially for these routes. Since the later fleet of standard Bo-Bo locomotives was based on the initial locomotives, the Bo-Bo layout is proving a somewhat limiting factor in the use of their full power output when they have to climb relatively steep gradients. At the time of writing, a new Co-Co arrangement was being considered for freight work.

At the time of the placing of the orders for the initial AC locomotives there was no recent British experience to draw on, although some of the electrical manufacturers did have experience of EMU train sets. In conjunction with industry, BR opted for DC traction motors with AC-DC conversion rectifiers. Mercury-arc rectifiers were used on classes 81 to 84, as it was considered that the semi-conductor rectifier had not sufficient experience in traction application to justify adoption. In the rosy light of hindsight, one would ask if mercury-arc rectifiers at that time were properly considered as being suitable to withstand the very demanding traction environment of being mounted on 100mph vehicles.

So far as mechanical design was concerned, the following limitations posed severe restraints on the manufacturers: the British loading gauge; the demand that 48in diameter wheels be used; the flat and lower roof to accommodate the pantographs and roof equipment and a 20-ton maximum axle load.

The main British electrical companies with experience in electric rail traction were instructed to follow their own lines of development within a number of restrictions. This resulted in a range of locomotives with a most definite family likeness, due to the BTC design panel dictates. The locomotives had a standard cab and cab layout, they used some items of auxiliary equipment as standard, and their performance characteristics were similar.

A total of 100 locomotives was ordered to five basic designs, although variations within some of these to try out alternative techniques was allowed. The BTC specified that their performance had to be within the following parameters:

Haulage	Max. Speed	Balancing Speed on level
	mph	mph
475 tons express passenger	100	90
500 tons express freight	60	—
1000 tons slow freight	55	—
Local passenger	75	—

To obtain full flexibility, mostly mixed traffic locomotives were decided upon, 80 of a type 'A' locomotive, and 20 of a type 'B' locomotive. The latter were to have different gear ratios to increase drawbar pull at the expense of maximum speed, with the idea that once all freight stock was fully brake-fitted, mineral trains would be hauled at a relatively high speed by type B locomotives.

British industry received orders for 60 complete locomotives, and 40 sets of equipment for locomotives to be built by BR workshops. The initial distribution was as follows:

Main Contractor	Locomotive Builder	Type of Locomotive	Number of Locomotives	Number of Locomotives in revised order
AEI (BTH)	BRCW	A	20	23
AEI (BTH)	BRCW	B	5	2
AEI (BTH)	BR	A	40	40
EE	VF	A	10	12
EE	VF	B	5	3
GEC	NBL	A	5	10
GEC	NBL	B	5	—
AEI (MV)	BP	A	5	10
AEI (MV)	BP	B	5	—
		TOTALS	100	100

Abbreviations

AEI	Associated Electrical Industries Ltd
BTH	British Thomson Houston Co Ltd
BRCW	Birmingham Railway Carriage & Wagon Co Ltd
BP	Beyer, Peacock & Co Ltd
EE	English Electric Co Ltd
NBL	North British Locomotive Co Ltd
VF	Vulcan Foundry Ltd
GEC	General Electric Co Ltd
MV	Metropolitan Vickers Electrical Co Ltd

To assist in identification, the revised order for locomotives were classified and numbered as follows:

Class	Builders		Type	Number Series
AL1	AEI (BTH)	BRCW	A	E3001-23
AL1	AEI (BTH)	BRCW	B	E3301/2
AL2	AEI (MV)	BP	A	E3046-55
AL3	EE	VF	A	E3024-35
AL3	EE	VF	B	E3303-5
AL4	GEC	NBL	A	E3036-45
AL5	AEI (BTH)	BR	A	E3056-95

At an early stage it was intended to number the BR AC locomotive fleet from E1 upwards, E1-40 being intended for class AL5. This would have introduced a system similar to that adopted for diesel locomotives. The idea was dropped to make way for one in which the locomotive running numbers gave an indication of the locomotive's rating in horsepower.

During the design stages, weight calculations revealed that axle loadings were being exceeded, so a considerable amount of redesign and alteration of equipment took place, with resulting delays in deliveries of locomotives. All locomotives incorporated bogie-frame mounted traction motors necessitating flexible drives to reduce to a minimum the unsprung weight on the axles, axle-hung traction motors being thought unsuitable.

All locomotives of the initial orders, except one, had the same pantographs. These were of Stone-Faiveley type derived, with modification, from a design used in France on the SNCF, two pantographs per locomotive being fitted. The pantographs known as the BR type AM-BR were manufactured in the UK under licence from Etablissements L. Faiveley, Paris. The main factor leading to the adoption of the Faiveley pantograph was its saving of roof mounting space on electric multiple units, where the 'knuckle end' was able to overhang the vehicle roof of normal height. This meant that it was not always necessary to mount the pantograph on a large lowered area of roof, saving considerable internal headroom and consequently passenger accommodation space. Other virtues were its low maintenance cost from roller or ball-bearings in the main joint of the mechanism, and a good record of current collection at high speeds. It was the first point which was most important to BR for its AC

locomotives, because with the large wheel size specified and loading gauge restrictions, the internal headroom of the locomotive equipment areas was considerably reduced. The normal height of 16ft 0in above track level varies in practice from 13ft 6in to 19ft 0in as required to take account of over-line structures, level-crossings, etc.

The many locations where the overhead wire has to negotiate crossovers at junctions necessitated the use of a curved pan head able to collect current over a width of 5ft 3in, and an arrangement to avoid pantograph tilting in the reverse direction. Contact pressure was set at 20lb, and took full account of static force and aerodynamics at 100mph. Raising and lowering of the pantograph is by an air motor indirectly controlled by the driver, the lifting speed being set to lessen the impact of the pantograph on the wire. Lowering the pantograph is carried out quickly until about 12in above the fully down position; at this point descent is slow until the final position is reached.

Brown-Boveri roof-mounted ABCBs were specified for 90 of the first AC locomotives. The 10 locomotives of AEI (MV) class AL2 units had the British AEI circuit breaker which was also installed on some multiple units for comparative trials with the continental equipment. In the air-blast system, as the circuit breaker is tripped compressed air is supplied to the arc and drawn between the fixed and moving contacts inside a chamber. As the contacts separate, the blast of air bends the arc path until it is too long to be sustained. Some BR AC locomotives have vacuum circuit breakers (VCB) which operate more quickly and are easier to maintain.

The main earthing switch on all BR AC vehicles, having the principles of mechanical interlocking for access to high-voltage compartments, was standardised so that no differences in protective methods for maintenance staff could cause errors. Any personnel operating the earthing switch on an AC locomotive could lock this in the safe earth position with a personal padlock before entering the high tension (HT) compartment.

In the first order, 90 locomotives had Buchholz gas-relay protective devices, which detected gas being formed by a fault in the transformer.

The 10 class AL2 locomotives had differential current protection which compared the output and input of the main transformer. All manufacturers used a similar fault indication

The first new AC locomotive delivered to BR was
E3001 of class AL1, later 81. Here the locomotive is
seen on a test train, and is in the original electric blue
livery with raised polished numbers, and BR lion-and-
wheel crest.   *(GEC Traction)*

panel so that in spite of equipment variations, the
warning given to the locomotive crew was similar.
The driver's control desk fault light glows bright
when any protective circuit operates. If the fault
light remains bright the fault indication panel will
usually indicate the circuit involved. The driver
can cut out individual traction motors and rectifier
equipments, and change fuses or reset miniature
circuit breakers if cooling fans or other auxiliaries
fail. The BR AC classes 81 to 85 originally had one
large air compressor and air receiver mounted
inside the locomotive.

Although orders were placed for the 100
locomotives in the mid-1950s, progress made
indicated that it would be some time before actual
delivery, and the 1958-60 period in fact became
1959-64.

To provide maintenance facilities for the AC
locomotive fleet, Crewe works was in due course
provided with special areas for heavy overhaul,
and a number of district electric depots was
proposed. Crewe depot opened in 1959 as a four-
track depot which in 1978 had an allocation of
classes 84 and 85, and also recommissions
locomotives from Crewe works.

Manchester Longsight is a two-road depot with
a wooden frame of laminated timber; this depot in
1978 had classes 82 and 83 on its allocation.
Liverpool Allerton had no permanent AC
locomotive allocation in 1978. The largest depot is
Willesden in north-west London, opened in 1965,

which in 1978 had the entire classes 86 and 87
allocated to it.

A depot at Birmingham called Soho was
proposed but not built, while a depot at Rugby was
opened and subsequently used for another
purpose. Bletchley depot has an allocation of
EMUs, but also produces pantograph heads for
multiple units and locomotives.

Anglo-Scottish electrification proposals saw
Carlisle Kingmoor depot opened in January
1968, initially as a diesel depot, but from 1973 also
for electric locomotives, and Glasgow Shields
Road depot in 1974. Kingmoor had no AC
locomotive allocation, but Shields Road had class
81 allocated to it in 1974; these remained there in
1978.

As part of the driver training programme in
readiness for the major extension of electrification
south to London in 1965 an electric locomotive
simulator was built at Willesden depot. The
equipment consisted of a mock-up cab with
standard controls, a moving display of the line
ahead through the cab; windows, including signal
aspects coinciding with signals as they appeared
on the screen, which could be switched by the
instructor to any normal sequence. There were
also sound and movement effects including, for
example, buffering up behind the locomotive by a
heavy handed brake application on a freight train
simulation, or an emergency brake application by
non-acknowledgement of an AWS warning.

CHAPTER 5

CLASS 81 (AL1)

The electrical manufacturer to receive the largest order for AC electric locomotive equipment from BR was Associated Electrical Industries Ltd (AEI). AEI was formed by the amalgamation of the British Thomson Houston Co Ltd of Rugby (BTH) and the Metropolitan Vickers Electrical Co Ltd, Manchester (MV). Although these two companies had worked closely together for many years, they received quite separate orders from BR, namely BTH 25 complete locomotives and 40 sets of equipment, and MV 10 complete locomotives, the total order accruing to AEI being 75.

The fact that BTH and MV relied on the Attercliffe Common (Sheffield) works of MV to manufacture items like traction motors often resulted in standardisation, which was apparent in

the AC locomotive work for BR, 75 locomotives having the same traction motors.

The AEI (BTH) locomotives were the first AC type to commence delivery to BR, being classified AL1, later 81, and numbered E3001-23/96/7. Both types A and B locomotives were originally included in the order, the mechanical part of which was sub-contracted to the Birmingham Railway Carriage & Wagon Co Ltd (BRCW), which built them at its Smethwick works in Birmingham. The gearing for the two type B locomotives was not used, and the equipment delivered to BR as spare to requirements.

Following BRCW practices with BR diesel-electric classes 26, 27 and 33, the mechanical parts were designed as a weight-carrying structure based on the body sides. The body sides are of

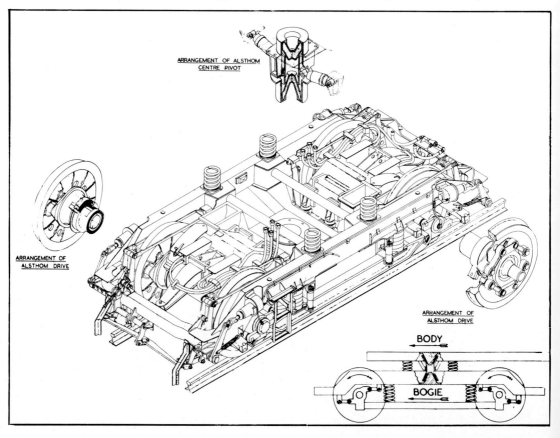

ARRANGEMENT OF ALSTHOM CENTRE PIVOT

ARRANGEMENT OF ALSTHOM DRIVE

ARRANGEMENT OF ALSTHOM DRIVE

BODY

BOGIE

Left: This type of bogie was used on the majority of BR AC locomotives. Classes 81, 85 and 86/0 have the Alsthom rubber cone centre-pivot, the four secondary coil springs, and in the case of classes 81, 82 and 85 the Alsthom final drive linkages to the wheels.
The inset side elevation of the bogie shows the centre cone, the secondary springs and the radius-arm guided axleboxes fitted to classes 81, 85, 86/0 and 86/2.

(British Rail)

Above: Class 81 bogie

A Westinghouse brake cylinder slack adjuster which automatically adjusts the brake cylinder piston rod stroke as the brake blocks wear down.

B Brake cylinder actuated by compressed air.

C Primary springs, outer spring only shown. Eight springs per bogie to carry the weight of the locomotive bogie on the equalising beams (J) and on the bottom of the axle boxes via rubber mountings.

D Secondary coil springs underneath rubbing pads on underside of locomotive body. Four units per bogie.

E Automatic power control (APC) magnetic switch and reset coil actuated by trackside magnets at neutral sections.

F Roller bearing axlebox showing earth connections to brush inside the box. The brush passes the return current from the locomotive main transformer via the axles and wheels to the track.

G Upper Alsthom axlebox radial link, lower link can be seen on near side of axlebox.

H Primary hydraulic damper to control action of primary springs. Four dampers per bogie.

J Equalising beam between axleboxes to equalise weight transfer during starting and stopping.

(John Duncan)

lattice girder construction with vertical and diagonal I-section members. The sides are braced together by cross-members at roof and floor level, forming a rigid box structure to support the main frame and traction equipment.

The main frame is of hollow box-section members and solebars, being built-up by welding from 8in × 3½in channels longitudinally, and similar size angles and cross-members. The inner and outer solebars form continuous members at each side. Butt-welding joins these to the box-section headstocks, made from ⅜in-thick steel plate. The drag-box incorporates a draft-bar between the headstock and bolster. A recess in the centre of the frame takes the transformer, and from this recess run two channel longitudinals to each bolster. The body floor is of 12-gauge steel plate throughout. The superstructure is clad with steel sheeting of 12-gauge.

In order to meet the requirement to mount certain items of equipment and the pantographs outside the locomotive body on the roof, in common with all BR AC locomotives, the roof of the equipment compartment had to be flat and considerably lower than the cab roofs. This resulted in a low internal headroom, and provided an unusual effect aesthetically. To give the required aesthetic appearance, false roof-side valances are fitted between the cab roofs to minimise to a great extent the stepped-down centre portion so far as the observer is concerned, and also masking roof mounted equipment. The recessed area is drained for snow and water-shedding purposes. Class 81 has its equipment compartment roof made in five sections, some in steel, some in glass-fibre. These sections are to provide access to equipment during maintenance. The sections together with the carrying transverse members are detachable.

On the corridor side of the locomotive body are placed four fixed windows with polished surrounds, and on the opposite side nine louvred air-intakes. The intakes do not have filters, the louvres themselves acting as baffles against coarse dirt and water particle ingress.

The drivers' cabs are of steel construction and have a double-skin glass-fibre roof canopy. The windscreen in all the first 100 AC locomotives, and the subsequent class 86, is in three sections, a layer of gold-film laminated into the glass, providing an electric heating element for demisting and de-icing. Although class 85 had wire demisters in a double-glazed arrangement, this is now being altered to laminated gold-film type. Windscreen wipers are fitted, and at one period some early locomotives had 'ship type' rotating glass wipers. Cab doors — two per cab — have drop windows. All the first 100 AC locomotives incorporated the then standard 4-digit train identification box in

the lower cab front panels, indicator and marker lights being fitted in their usual positions.

The bogie design of class 81 was based on Alsthom ideas, and introduced for the first time in a BR locomotive the Alsthom rubber cone pivot for body suspension, the same system being used in the prototype 2750bhp Co-Co diesel-electric locomotive by BRCW-Sulzer-AEI D0260 *Lion*. The Alsthom radius-arm guided axleboxes, also applied to *Lion*, and flexible link drive were used on class 81.

The bogies themselves are fabricated by welding from box-section hollow units to form the main members and solebars; underslung equalising beams of welded Cor-Ten steel fabrications are fitted. Four nests of double-coil helical springs support the bogie frame from the equalising beams. Shock-absorbers are provided, and primary springing is thereby controlled to maintain the clearances for the Alsthom quill drive of the traction motors. The equalising beams are

Below left: Class 81 main transformer before installation. The main tank houses the transformer winding immersed in pure mineral oil. This provides insulation and cooling via pipework on other side of the transformer. Radiators, pipework, pump, and header tank (conservator) are not shown.

    A Two thermostatic switches, one set at 85⁰C as a warning, and the second at 95⁰C to trip the ABCB.
    B Temperature thermostats.
    C 25000V input terminal with its large insulator.
    D Secondary output terminals.
    E Voltage changeover equipment for 6.25/25kV operation (not used).
    F Mounting frame for fixing at locomotive floor level.

    G Bottom of transformer tank which passes through the locomotive floor between the bogies, giving a lower centre of gravity and assisting locomotive stability.   *(GEC Traction)*

Below right: Class 81 air-cooled steel-tank type mercury arc rectifier, of which three were fitted to each locomotive until conversion to silicon rectifiers. Class 82 employed similar units.
    A The six anode connections (AC) with the excitation and protection equipment.
    B The cathode connection (rectified DC).
    (GEC Traction)

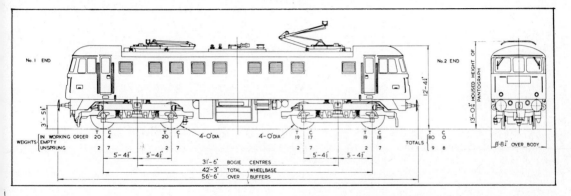

Diagram of class 81, as originally built with two
pantographs.   *(British Rail)*

carried on combined shear/compression rubber
pads on the Skefco (SKF) roller-bearing
axleboxes. This, with the fully-sprung traction
motors, considerably reduces dead weight on the
track.

There are no fixed guides for the axleboxes;
instead two Silenthoc-bushed radius arms
anchored to the bogie frames control fore-and-aft
forces and also give some lateral resilience to
reduce wheel flange wear.

The Alsthom secondary suspension consists of a
vertical column between the underframe and the
fixed bogie bolster, having large rubber conical
bearings at both ends. Locomotive tractive effort
is transmitted through the rubber, and by
manganese bearing pads in the central column.
Side movement is controlled by pre-loaded
double-acting springs. Four coil springs take part
of the body weight. The Alsthom system offers an
almost roll-free locomotive body, and the system
allows adjustment as required to equalise
loadings.

The internal layout comprises two compartments housing the main equipment. Access to the
control gear, rectifiers, and transformer is only
possible when the pantograph is down and the HT
equipment earthed. An interlocking door governs
this. The compartment housing transformer and
rectifiers is caged in full height lattice wire
grill.

Voltage changeover equipment was included
but never used. The main transformer had its
primary winding in four sections connected in
series for 25kV and parallel for 6.25kV. This was
done automatically by an oil-immersed off load
changeover switch. Transformer oil cooling

employs two Serck radiators fitted under the roof,
two Aerex fans drawing in the air through
bodyside louvres over the vertical radiator panels
and discharge through the roof.

Two Stone-Faiveley pantographs were fitted
originally to 99 BR AC locomotives in the first
orders, the current being fed through roof-
mounted Brown-Boveri (BB) air-blast circuit
breakers to the main transformer in 90 locos.

The output from the main transformer is
converted from AC to DC for the traction motors
originally by three air-cooled, six-anode pumpless
steel-tank mercury arc rectifiers, diametrically
connected in parallel so that each tank had three
anodes in each half cycle. The rectifiers were
mounted side by side in an airtight compartment
and were carried on resilient mountings placed
close to their centre of gravity. Of a well-tried type,
the rectifiers had modified cathodes to minimise
splashing of the mercury pool under traction
conditions and with an ignition device designed
for frequent operation. Current was shared
between the tanks and anodes by load-sharing
reactors; smoothing chokes were also fitted.
Rectifier cooling was individually controlled by an
automatic system, an Aerex fan drawing air into a
duct to the base of the rectifier and then upwards to
discharge through the roof.

When the locomotive first went on line the
bodyside shutters were closed and the heater panel
shutters opened. Air was circulated by the fan on a
closed circuit through the heater and the rectifier.
At the appropriate temperature, thermostats
switched off the heater; the rectifiers were then
heated by passing a low voltage current through
them. When normal working temperature was
reached, the heater was switched off and as higher
air temperatures occurred, more thermostats
closed the heater panel shutters and opened
cooling air inlet shutters in the bodyside.

Class 81, 81014, in 1978 condition at Carlisle
Kingmoor Depot.   (Brian Webb)

To improve traction motor commutation, the AC ripple is reduced by employing non-inductive resistances across the field coils. This enables most of the AC component to be bypassed. The traction motor poles are connected by a laminated ring inside the main yoke casting to keep the inter-pole flux and armature current in phase. The original iron-cored smoothing chokes through which the motors are fed relied on natural air convection to cool them.

Control equipment comprises a camshaft unit operated by the driver's master controller with 40 accelerating notches. Voltage control is by on-load tap changing on the low voltage side, and the output is fed to the rectifiers via a pair of high-speed circuit or line breakers, which makes anode fuses unnecessary. The breakers protect against rectifier back-firing and also act as contactors during normal operation of the locomotive, so no individual motor contactors are required. Back firing is current being passed by the rectifier in wrong half-cycle, which creates a short circuit on the transformer winding.

Two traction motor blowers, three rectifier cooling fans, two transformer cooling oil radiator fans, and the transformer oil circulating pump are driven by AC motors. One exhauster is fed by the locomotive battery, the other and the compressor is fed by the AC supply through separate germanium rectifiers.

The battery is continually fed from a battery charger of the magnestat type incorporating a germanium rectifier. A small battery fed Clayton auxiliary air-compressor is used for raising the pantograph, when the main air-reservoir is empty.

The four traction motors are AEI (BTH) type 189 with a continuous rating of 975V, 700A, 847hp; one-hour rating being 975V, 760A, 920hp. Gear ratios for the 23 type A locomotives was 29:76, and the two type B units 26:83, in the latter case not fitted. The motors are connected permanently in parallel; they are six-pole series wound machines with forced ventilation and class 'H' insulation. One traction motor blower is fitted behind each driving cab rear bulkhead, each supplying cooling air to the two motors on the nearest bogie. The traction motors are fully frame-mounted with 3-point Metalastik pre-loaded rubber springs, two conical ones at the nose to locate the motor against movement in the bogie frame, and another between an extension arm from the motor frame and the bogie headstock. No vertical thrust is transmitted directly to the axles.

The motor reduction gearing drives through a hollow shaft to a universal link assembly, which has four Alsthom links each end with Silentbloc bushes, thus eliminating lubrication; these drive the wheel. The drive ends of one pair of links are attached to the hollow shaft of the reduction gear, and the ends of the other pair to drive pins on the wheels. The inner ends of the four links are anchored to a floating ring on the outside of the wheel. This system gives a cushioned resilient drive between the traction motor and the wheel, permitting the axle vertical movement.

Brake gear of the Westinghouse type was fitted throughout initially, air brake for the locomotive, and vacuum brake only for the train.

Class 81 protective devices included a Buchholz relay in the main transformer to protect against earth faults, warn of short circuits in the transformer and indicate low transformer oil levels, acting by opening the air-blast circuit breaker. Surge protection was provided. High transformer oil temperatures also caused tripping of the air-blast circuit breaker.

Rectifiers had back-fire protection by high-speed circuit breakers in rectifier anode feeds;

surge protection was again provided. Overload relays in each traction motor circuit tripped the line circuit breakers. For earth faults the system is solidly earthed at rectifier cathodes and a relay operating from a current transformer trips the circuit breaker.

A general alarm light in the locomotive cab, plus the fault-indicating panel inside the locomotive body, covered the following conditions: motor overloads tripped, earth fault, transformer oil excessive temperature, traction motor blowers stopped, rectifier temperature wrong, rectifier not exciting, Buchholz alarm. Motor overloads, earth faults, transformer excessive temperature, rectifier back-fire, high transformer oil temperature and Buchholz operation leave a flagged indication for maintenance staff.

The high tension (HT) equipment compartment in the earlier locomotive classes has access through one door on classes 81-83/5, two on 84, these doors being interlocked with the pantograph air valve and roof earthing switch. It was only possible to enter the HT compartment with the pantographs down and equipment earthed. Six of the axle ends have earthing brushes insulated from the axleboxes, four brushes being connected to the earth side of the transformer primary and two to the locomotive frame. The auxiliary circuits are earthed through the frame. The two remaining axles are fitted with speedometer and mileometer drives.

Although voltage detection/selection equipment for 6.25/25kV operation was fitted, it was never used on BR AC locomotives, since the West Coast main line was found not to need 6.25kV as full clearance for 25kV was obtainable, particularly after relaxation of clearance to a minimum of 8in above and below the live wires. As a result the circuits were disconnected and are no longer operational.

All BR's AC locomotives with mercury-arc rectifiers proved troublesome, some more than others, depending on the individual choice of the manufacturer concerned. Semi-conductor rectifiers were not at the time proven, and the grades of silicon and germanium were not of sufficient purity, so all concerned took the 'devil-you-know' attitude.

In class 81 the multiple-anode rectifiers with air-cooling were troublesome; ignition circuit difficulties were common in classes 81 and 82. In class 81 the rectifiers were preheated by a rectifier short-circuit arrangement, and with space heaters

and thermostatically controlled louvres. An improved thermostat technique resulted in ability to dispense with the short circuit scheme, and the space heaters were found sufficient to bring the rectifiers up to working temperature level. Class 81, in common with class 82 and the germanium-equipped class 85, was converted to silicon rectifiers at Crewe works.

The AEI 189 traction motor has a liability to flashovers. Being a six-pole machine of considerable power, it has the brush boxes closer together than in a four-pole machine. Access to the connecting rings between brush boxes makes maintenance difficult and dirty conditions cause breakdown and flashovers. During 1972 the 189 traction motor fitted to classes 81 and 85 experienced the first of a number of compole failures. In this traction motor the compoles were connected electrically on the positive side of the armatures so that should an armature flashover, there would be some resistance, albeit small, in the fault path. The compole coils, although bare, were fully insulated for the expected voltages. However, a spate of failures of compole insulation to earth revealed the existence of a problem which was finally traced and eliminated in a rather interesting manner. The space available for the compoles between the six main poles was somewhat limited; when the compole coils took the very heavy currents resulting from fault conditions, they tried to become circular instead of rectangular in accordance with the laws of electromagnetism. The middle of the coil moved outwards and, because of the small clearances, sometimes came into contact with the main poles which were of course earthed.

The cure was very simple, namely to tie them so that they could not move under fault currents. This was achieved by machining two slots in the compoles themselves and using the slots to locate two bands which were wound around the complete compole coils. The material of the bands was resin impregnated glass-fibre as used in modern armature banding practice. After application to the hot compole, the assembly was baked when the resin ran, and then set hard to form a very strong monolithic band, which is also an excellent insulating material. Interestingly, the 189 motors used on class 82 have not given trouble in this way, being connected differently.

Originally the 81s had large smoothing chokes which projected downwards under the loco-motive, being cooled naturally by the air flow-

Comparative diagrams of classes 81 and 82 showing
the 1978 layout.   *(British Rail)*

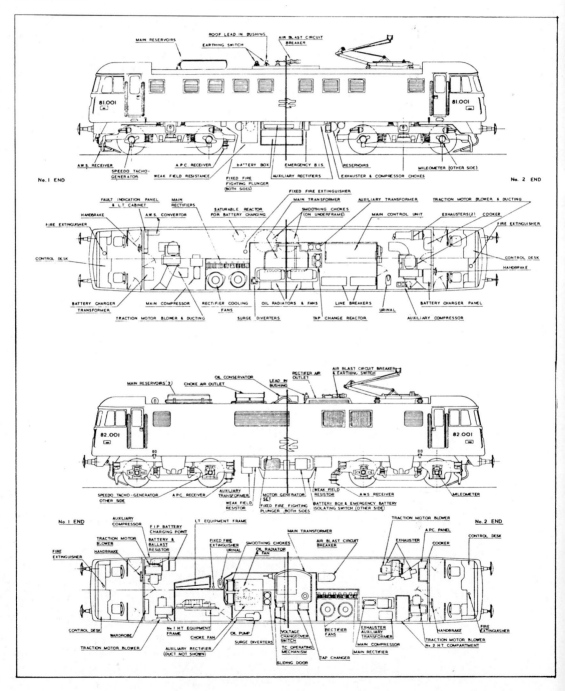

ing around them while the locomotive was moving. The locomotives worked well until they were used on the hilly extensions over Shap and Beattock, when the choke cooling was found to be inadequate. New and smaller smoothing chokes were fitted, force-cooled by fans, which worked well. During the hot 1976 summer the new electronic temperature sensing protecting the chokes gave some trouble, but modifications to this equipment are now proving successful.

The lower power (¼hp) tap changer motor became inadequate when camshaft modifications were carried out to eliminate excessive contact wear. A new ½hp unit by Normend is running trials in the similarly-equipped class 85, in place of the original motor, and is likely to be fitted throughout the fleet to prevent camshafts stalling; 85001 is the locomotive concerned.

In class 81 two large high-speed line contractors gave trouble during the early days. They were fitted by the makers, who considered them better than motor contactors in restricting back-firing of the mercury-arc rectifiers. When first in service they sometimes failed to close and occasionally welded contacts together.

Class 81 locomotives suffer from 'body lean' caused by the unequal height of the four body support springs, resulting in side-to-side or lateral movement during which the locomotive body moves over and makes contact with the rubber bogie-lateral stop, giving a slapping action. The modifications in hand for the rough riding correction are the fitting of ferro-bestos pads which restrict slide, in place of the manganese pads originally fitted.

The high number of complaints received from drivers about the notoriously bad riding qualities of class 81 prompted a series of comparative tests

Condition Number	Date of test	Locomotive No.	Condition of Locomotive
—	10/10/77	81019	Ex-service
1	11/10/77	81001	Ex-service
2	13/10/77	81001	New centre pivot rubbers
3	14/10/77	81001	As above but with new primary dampers
—	17/10/77	81005	Ex-works after full repairs
4	18/10/77	81001	As condition 3, but with new centre pivot stabilisers
5	24/10/77	81001	As condition 4, but with new greased secondary springs, side bearer packings, ferro-bestos pads on side bearer pockets.

between Glasgow and Beattock on the WCML during October 1977. The programme involved locomotives in various conditions as shown in the accompanying table.

81001/19 were taken straight from service for comparison with 81005 in ex-works condition. In the case of 81001 the tests were repeated after maintenance work on the suspension, this being done at Glasgow Shields depot in four stages, with tests at each stage.

An 11-coach test train was used at speeds up to 90mph, instrumentation being provided in the leading cab of the locomotive on up runs, and trailing cab in the down direction. Accelerometers in the centre of the cab floor recorded the vertical, lateral and longitudinal ride. Tests showed that 81001/19 in ex-service condition gave a very bad ride vertically and laterally at crossovers, points and at rail joints, while body bounce in the vertical plane was severe. A degree of under-damping was diagnosed. To ascertain the effects of the four stages of alterations on 81001's suspension, tests were run for comparison with previous runs. It was found that in condition 2 the new rubbers made no improvement, condition 3 made the most significant improvement, while condition 5 gave a further small improvement, all in vertical riding. Lateral riding was improved by maintenance at 5, when three points were covered: (a)—new greased secondary springs, (b)—packings inserted on one side of the locomotive to level the body, and (c)—fitting ferro-bestos pads in side bearer sockets instead of the manganese pads normally fitted. The cumulative effect was improvement on lateral riding, it being considered that the ferro-bestos pads were the main contribution to the improvement.

In January 1978 further methods of improving the ride were investigated: (a)—fitting of an extra primary damper at each position on the bogie, (b)—investigation of the likely effect of weight redistribution between bogie centre pivot and side bearer. The former was to be tried by the Scottish Region, but investigation into the latter was thought too detailed at the time.

All BR AC locomotives were fitted with bromochlorodifluoro-methane (BCF) fixed fire-fighting equipment from 1970, plus emergency battery isolation switches outside the locomotives. The system is manually operated by a pull handle at each side of the locomotive on the underframe. Also from 1970 dual braking and silicon rectifiers were fitted to class 81.

The first class 81, E3001, was handed-over officially to BR at Sandbach Station on 27 November 1959; this was the first completely new AC locomotive built for BR. Actual deliveries of class 81 occupied the period December 1959 to February 1964, the first pair E3001/2 being in use for crew-training on the Styal line by February 1960, working from their stabling point at East Didsbury. As deliveries proceeded from BRCW, locomotives were towed to Rugby where they were stored, pending fitting of some final items of equipment, in a portion of the Rugby repair shops of BR. The locomotives were issed for acceptance trials from there and then put on crew-training along with locomotives of other manufacturers. In July 1960 those delivered were officially allocated to Manchester (Longsight) depot.

From September they shared some Manchester-Crewe services, together with steam and diesel traction, working main line and local trains, often in tandem. By March 1961 construction had reached E3020. Subsequently the class was given the general LMR AC line allocation, this continuing until the 1972-5 period when various locomotives were temporarily located at Carlisle Kingmoor and Glasgow Shields Road depots for training purposes, pending introduction of Anglo-Scottish electric services. All remained at Crewe until March 1975 when they transferred to Glasgow Shields Road depot, where they remain the Scottish Region's only AC locomotive allocation.

Their work is now mostly on freight and some overnight sleeping car train duties. Future plans for class 81 may include fitting for push-and-pull working, and transfer to the ER for use on the Great Eastern section between London (Liverpool Street) and Ipswich as part of a plan to eliminate diesel traction from that London terminus. The main problems presenting a serious threat to this plan are the poor riding at 100mph and the expense of the ETH circuit modifications for handling the latest coaching stock.

Three class 81s have been withdrawn. E3002/19 were burnt-out by severe fires in 1968 and 1971, due in one case possibly to the locomotive being accidentally put into reverse at high speed and causing the traction motors to regenerate and overheat. The resulting fires in the motors spread to the complete locomotive. All locomotives now have a special button on the master controller which must be operated to enable reverse to be selected; this has been

successful in preventing further incidents. The third locomotive, E3009, was involved in the Hixon level-crossing accident on 6 January 1968, when the locomotive and its train collided at high speed with a low-loader lorry carrying a heavy transformer. This accident on an unmanned level-crossing with automatic barriers caused BR and the Ministry of Transport to rethink automatic level-crossing policy, to prevent a recurrence.

CLASS 81 (AL1) NUMBERING AND CONSTRUCTION DETAILS
Main contractor: AEI (BTH)
Builder of locomotives: Birmingham Railway Carriage & Wagon Co Ltd (BRCW)

Original Number	New Number	AEI (BTH) Works Number	Date into Traffic
E3001	81001	1083	P12/59
E3002	—	1084	P1/60
E3003	81002	1085	P2/60
E3004	81003	1086	P4/60
E3005	81004	1087	P5/60
E3006	81005	1088	P7/60
E3007	81006	1089	P8/60
E3008	81007	1090	P10/60
E3009	—	1091	P10/60
E3010	81008	1092	P11/60
E3011	81009	1093	P12/60
E3012	81010	1094	P12/60
E3013	81011	1095	P12/60
E3014	81012	1096	P13/60
E3015	81013	1097	P13/60
E3016	81014	1098	P3/61
E3017	81015	1099	P5/61
E3018	81016	1100	P3/61
E3019	—	1101	P4/61
E3020	81017	1102	P5/61
E3021	81018	1103	P6/61
E3022	81019	1104	P10/61
E3023	81020	1105	P2/62
E3096	81021	1106	P6/62
E3097	81022	1107	P2/64

NOTES

AEI works numbers 1188-1212 also allocated.
E3096/7 were allocated type B numbers E3301/2, but did not carry them.
E3002   withdrawn P11/68. Severe fire damage
E3009   withdrawn P8/68.   Hixon level crossing collision 6/1/68
E3019   withdrawn P7/71.   Severe fire damage at Stockport Edgeley.

CHAPTER 6

CLASS 82 (AL2)

The AEI (MV) contribution to the BR AC locomotive fleet was class AL2, subsequently reclassified 82. Numbered E3046-E3055 they were ordered from MV at Trafford Park, Manchester, and MV being part of AEI the locomotives were standardised in some respects of their equipment with the AEI (BTH) locomotives of class 81 and with the BR-built AEI (BTH)-equipped class 85 locomotives.

The whole of the design of class 82 was by MV, but the manufacture of the mechanical parts and erection of the locomotives was sub-contracted to Beyer, Peacock & Co Ltd of Manchester which carried out the work at its Gorton Foundry Locomotive works.

Mechanically, class 82 demonstrates the separate underframe, separate body type of construction, as opposed to the integral structure of other classes. The former takes all the horizontal and vertical loadings, the body only performing as a light protective container to house the electrical equipment.

The superstructure was not built as

economically as possible, because of weight problems dictating its largely alloy and glass-fibre construction. The strength required for load-carrying is provided by the very stiff underframe which is a welded assembly of steel plate and rolled-steel sections; the side plates between the bogies are 2ft 0in deep. Aluminium alloy ⅛in thick is used for bodyside panels. This is riveted to light-alloy rails and pillars. The floor-plate decking was originally of glass-fibre but from 1972 was modified on some locomotives to aluminium and steel plate. The body structure is attached by bracing to the transformer tank top plate to give it rigidity. On the corridor side of the body are two fixed windows and on the other side three air inlets with louvres made of glass-fibre, which were modified in 1972. The roof was mostly of translucent glass-fibre but is now aluminium, and is detachable for maintenance access to internal equipment. The drivers' cabs have an outer skin of aluminium, and are timber-lined, with plastic laminate-faced aluminium sheet. The cab roof is a double-skin glass-fibre moulding.

The first AL2, E3046, now class 82, standing in the works yard of Beyer, Peacock & Co Ltd at Gorton, Manchester. *(GEC Traction)*

Above: E3048, with cab-front yellow warning panel, on a freight train. *(GEC Traction)*

Below: Class 82 bogie, the only cast-steel bogie fitted to a BR AC class.

A Brake rod to the inner brake hanger from the vertical pivoting shaft on the corners of the bogie frame, the shafts are connected to a brake cylinder at each end of the bogie frame.

B Body side-member connected to body draw-buff beam which passes under the bogie to the side member on the opposite side. The traction links are connected to a beam from the kingpost in the centre of the bogie frame.

C APC magnetic switch and reset coil.

D Axlebox locating link connected to the axlebox to another link on the opposite side. The two links are connected to the frame, the links controlling the lateral movement of the axleboxes. One set of links is mounted on each side of the bogie, at alternate ends.

E Roller-bearing axlebox. Traction and braking forces are transmitted through conventional horns with manganese steel liners. Note the earthing brush connection and cable.

F Primary springs. **G** Primary damper.

H Equalising beam which transfers weight on to the top of each axlebox through Metalastik mountings.

J Axle-mounted speedometer generator (AEI type).

K Bottom of secondary suspension hanger which connects onto a spring cap, a beam then passing across the top of the bogie frame to an identical arrangement on the other side. Beneath the spring cap are the secondary coil springs. The traction and braking forces are taken through longitudinal links connecting the spring cap to the bogie frame at opposite corners. *(John Duncan)*

Commonwealth-type cast-steel bogie frames are employed for class 82, the only AC locomotive class so equipped. The frame is supported on four primary coil springs damped by their own hydraulic dampers. They have a transverse spring plank mounted resiliently to the bottom of the body support struts. The weight of the body is transmitted from the spring plank through four nests of secondary coil springs to the bogie frame. The centre pivot carries no weight, its sole purpose being to transmit at axle level the traction and braking forces only. Lateral movement is allowed by link anchorage of the pivot pin bush. Rubber seatings and bush pivot joints are on all suspension members, which are of the MV swing-link type. Timken tapered roller-bearing axleboxes are fitted, located laterally by rubber-bushed links anchored to the bogie frame.

Class 82 employs HT tap changing for main transformer secondary voltage output control to the traction motors. The advantage of HT tap changing is that relatively small currents are handled by the tap-changer and associated switches.

The main transformer is in the centre of the locomotive power compartment, with the rectifiers and cooling units at one end. At the other end are located the transformer radiator, smoothing chokes and control equipment frames. This equipment is enclosed by glass-fibre and aluminium panelling, and the HT compartment door has safety interlocking to prevent entry while pantographs are raised.

At No 1 bulkhead are two traction motor blowers, the air brake compressor, and a battery-powered auxiliary compressor to provide air pressure to close/open the air-blast circuit breaker and raise the pantograph. At the opposite end are two more traction motor blowers and the vacuum exhauster.

E3046-54 had two Stone-Faiveley pantographs, E3055 two AEI cross-arm pantographs.

The main transformer is placed in a vertical rectangular aluminium tank set in a shallow well in the locomotive underframe, but extending to roof level at the top. This provides bracing for the roof structure and makes it possible to eliminate the lead-in roof insulator, as the HT input terminal is mounted directly on the tank top. Oil cooling is used for the transformer, which is itself a combined unit of auto-transformer and a double-wound step-down transformer, both built partly

on a common core. Primary overload protection is provided, and instead of a Buchholz gas detecting device, class 82 uses a differential current relay which compares input and output currents. Cooling of the transformer oil is by 200 gallons/minute pumped circulation through a Serck radiator in the roof, air being blown through by a Keith-Blackman fan.

Tappings for auxiliary use are 800V for train heating and 240V for motors of auxiliary equipment. Because of deficiencies in the transformer tapping arising from fluctuations in the line voltage, battery charging proved unreliable and a motor generator set was fitted instead.

AC was converted to DC for the traction motors by three six-anode air-cooled steel tank mercury-arc rectifiers, and were identical to those used in class 81. Air cooling and heating by thermostatically controlled fans was also similar to class 81.

The four traction motors of AEI (BTH) type 189Z are standard with class 81, apart from a change in the mechanical design to reduce weight. The motors have one traction motor blower per traction motor, whereas the class 81 has one blower for each pair of motors. The motors have a continuous rating of 847hp, 975V, 700A. They are carried in the bogie frame by a three-point suspension with resilient rubber bushes; Alsthom drive is used.

Brake equipment was originally by Davies & Metcalfe and provided for the locomotive independent air brake, and vacuum-controlled air braking when hauling vacuum-braked trains. Air for the brakes came from a Worthington-Simpson compressor, and vacuum was provided by a Worthington-Simpson exhauster. For dual braking they were later fitted with Westinghouse 3VC75 main compressor, and Reavell rotary exhausters.

Class 82 protective measures are as follows. The primary winding of the main transformer is protected in the case of earth faults by the main circuit breaker and a differential relay supplied from current transformers at the HT and earth ends of the auto-transformer winding. Should the primary current earth return path be completely interrupted accidentally, a static earthing device connected to the 800V train heating tap comes into operation and connects this tap solidly to earth through the locomotive frame and wheels. A three-element overload relay is connected in each phase on the transformer secondary, one element being in series with each winding on the inter-tank reactors. These relays, when tripped, open the ABCB. Indication of rectifier backfires was given by polarised relays connected in series with each rectifier cathode. An overload relay in each traction motor circuit controls the motor contactors which isolate the motor.

For the low tension power circuit earth fault protection, a relay is provided which trips the circuit breaker if the rectifier cathode potential reaches approximately 36V above earth.

Surge diverters in series with spark gaps are connected across the transformer secondary winding and the DC load circuit and the surge diverters only across individual windings on the intertank reactors.

Fuses protect all auxiliary and control circuits, while voltage proving relays check the supply to the motors for the oil pump and essential cooling fans, a float switch opening the circuit-breaker if the transformer oil level falls below the set level.

The class 82 suffered initially from heavy brake gear maintenance costs arising largely because the brake rigging had no slack adjusters. A similar practice to steam locomotives was employed, with rods provided for brake adjustment, one rod per wheel, one brake cylinder per pair of wheels. The brake rigging suffered from binding and heavy brake block wear/flanging, when braking force

was not applied equally, resulting in some cases of the brake block and carrier turned completely over. Flanging was cured by fitting new carrier and modified hangers of split-type which held the blocks more rigidly, lateral movement of the hangers being dealt with by inserting pads. Automatic slack adjusters were also fitted.

Originally the brake rigging on class 82 was oil lubricated rather than grease-lubricated. It is possible that the oil lubricant was the source of the fire caused by brake blocks overheating and sparking, which resulted in locomotive E3055 being written-off by fire. In this case spark ignited the oil which was then sucked into the rectifier cooling intake by the fan above No 1 traction motor. E3046 was also burnt out, and although the cause could have been similar to that of E3055, it was believed to have been a traction motor power control failure. Interestingly, the remains of E3055 were stored for some years pending a decision on trials with either silicon rectifiers or thyristors in association with AEI, but these were eventually abandoned.

A problem arose in class 82 when the transformer cooling oil level in the roof tank was allowed to fall lower than was desirable. As the locomotives were running the oil was swilling about in the header tank and fluctuating in depth, thereby activating the Mobray float switch, tripping the air-blast circuit breaker and causing

Right: Class 82 main transformer which was mounted entirely within the locomotive body. In class 82 tap changing is done on the primary winding.

Key: **A** Conservator tank allows for a reserve of oil and expansion/contraction through a silica gell breather

B Mobray float switch which opens the ABCB when the oil in the conservator tank drops below the level of the switch.

C 25000V input terminal and insulator.

D Mounting joint for locomotive roof.

E Housing for tap changer motor, drive mechanism and cams to operate the diverter contactors.

F Two diverter contactors operated by rods from the tap changer camshaft above. The two large insulators are the tappings from the primary winding to the diverter contactors, and designed to make and break the inter tap loads as the sliding contacts inside the transformer move from one contact to the next.

G Base of transformer bolted to locomotive floor.

H Oil inlet connections.

J Secondary output terminals.

K Oil outlet connections.   *(GEC Traction)*

Right: E3054 nearing completion in the works of Beyer, Peacock & Co Ltd alongside a Brush 0-4-0DE industrial shunter being built under a subcontract from Brush for the British steel industry.

Key: **A** Number 2 end pantograph.

B Rectifier cooling air outlet ducting.

C 25000V input connection and insulator to the main transformer.

D AEI type of air-blast circuit breaker.

E Conservator oil tank to allow transformer oil to expand and contract.

F Roof over transformer radiator horizontally mounted at roof level.

G Voltage detection insulator for sensing the line voltage (not used).

H Number 1 end pantograph. This is now removed and three main air reservoirs fitted in its place.
                                         (GEC Traction)

Left: E3055, the only locomotive of the first 100 BR AC locomotives to have other than the Stone-Faiveley pantograph. E3055 had the AEI crossed-arm type.
                                         (GEC Traction)

82008 heading an up parcels train near Low Gill on 26
June 1976. The revised B side louvre arrangement is
clearly visible.   *(G.T. Heavyside)*

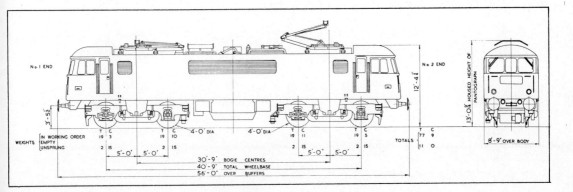

Diagram of class 82 as built with two pantographs and
original B side bodyside louvre arrangement.

(British Rail)

the locomotive to lose power. The circuit breaker
was reset and the locomotive would continue until
the next time the oil movement repeated the
problem.

The HT tap changing in class 82 uses an auto-
transformer which feeds into a fixed-ratio
winding. The high-voltage tapping contacts are
part of the main transformer tank and are under oil
with external breaking contactors for on-load tap
changing interlap currents. The tap changer
operates at up to 25kV, providing 38 voltage
tappings. There are 38 notches plus two weak field
stages. On class 82 the insulation board between
the tap change and transformer compartments
gave trouble by splitting in the event of a tap
changer failure.

During refurbishing, E3049 being the first
conversion of a locomotive from mercury-arc to
semi-conductor silicon rectifiers, the bodyside air
inlets were modified. Other alterations during the
1972-74 period were provision of sanding, fixed
fire-fighting equipment, windscreen washers, and
urinals instead of chemical toilets. These items
were also carried out on classes 81, 83, 84 and 85,
and to some extent on the second generation
locomotives, class 86.

Throughout the design and construction, class
82 was constantly up against weight problems.
This resulted in revision not only of mechanical
parts design by having to use more costly
lightweight materials for body construction than
was desirable, but also some change of electrical
equipment, and adoption of lighter units.

The first class 82 unit appeared in May 1960,
deliveries proceeding slowly up to the end of the
year, by which time seven were in traffic. The final
locomotives did not appear until 1962 because of

operating problems, notably ignition troubles
with the rectifiers, tap-changing problems and
weight-reduction exercises.

Their permanent allocations have always been
to Longsight depot, except for the period when
they were on general AC lines allocation, and when
some were used for crew-training during the 1972
and 1974 period.

In 1978 the eight survivors were still hard at
work, mainly on freight workings. The 82s have
proved to be one of the best riding of the first 100
locomotives, and their electrical circuits are by far
the simplest, which is helpful in achieving a
generally higher than average reliability for the
early classes of AC locomotives.

CLASS 82 (AL2) NUMBERING AND CONSTRUCTION DETAILS

Main contractor: Associated Electrical Industries
(Metropolitan Vickers AEI/MV)
Builder of locomotives: Beyer, Peacock & Co Ltd (BP)

Original Number	New Number	AEI (MV) Works No.	BP Works No.	Date into Traffic
E3046	—	1021	7884	P5/60
E3047	82001	1022	7885	P7/60
E3048	82002	1023	7886	P8/60
E3049	82003	1024	7887	P9/60
E3050	82004	1025	7888	P10/60
E3051	82005	1026	7889	P11/60
E3052	82006	1027	7890	P12/60
E3053	82007	1028	7891	P1/62
E3054	82008	1029	7892	P11/61
E3055	—	1030	7893	P4/62

NOTES

E3046 Withdrawn 1/71. Fire damage on 7/1/71
north of Bletchley on 15.45
Euston-Manchester

E3055 Withdrawn 9/69. Fire damage at Maw Green 1966.

CHAPTER 7
CLASS 83 (AL3)

The AC locomotives supplied by the English Electric Co Ltd were built at the Vulcan Foundry Ltd, Newton-le-Willows, Lancashire (VF), a member of the EE group, in 1960/61. Numbered E3024-35 as type A locomotive, and E3303-5 type B locomotives, they were noteworthy because of their light weight. Their power output rating was lower than that of other manufacturers' locomotives, but the gear ratios used by EE ensured that the required tractive effort was reached. The final locomotive, E3305, was built as E3100 and fitted with transductor control.

The mechanical design of class 83 is based on a frame and body fabricated as a stress-bearing unit from Cor-Ten steel. The underframe is an integral stress-bearing structure of shallow cellular construction built up from light gauge members. It is covered top and bottom to form a closed unit. Bodysides have girder frames and pillars of rectangular tubular sections covered with exterior and interior skins of steel sheeting. Cantrails are compound closed sections. The bodysides are tied transversely at roof level to form a very rigid structure, welding being used virtually throughout.

The use of steel, aluminium alloys, and glass-fibre materials largely dispensed with steel castings and their associated weight disadvantages. This use of lighter materials was due to the problem met by all locomotive builders, that of keeping weights down to specification. The use of glass-fibre with its costly moulds was not really a viable solution in a production run of only 15 locomotives.

As usual, the locomotive roof between the cab rear bulkheads is removable for maintenance. The interior headroom of class 83 is the best on a BR AC locomotive, the floor between the bogies being dished to give the advantage to the maintenance staff of being able to stand upright.

One locomotive superstructure was given structural and strain tests at the EE mechanical laboratories at Whetstone, Leicester, in June 1960, the body being sent back to VF on 13 February 1961 for use in locomotive E3100.

The bogies are conventional in design with side frames, transoms and headstocks, fabricated box-section construction, riveted together. A short equalising spring beam is pin joined to the underside of each roller bearing SKF axlebox. The primary coil springs rest in cups attached to this beam, and hydraulic dampers are fitted inside the springs. All the bogie components were placed to give accessibility, with all operating gear on the outside. Special care was taken to design a good riding bogie; long-range spring gear, swing bolsters, and close guiding of wheels and axles were used for this reason. To stop 'hunting', the vertical loading from the superstructure is transmitted in part through side bearers. Periodic oscillations of the swing bolsters are restrained by hydraulic dampers. The bolster has no friction plates, traction thrusts being transmitted by two links between bogie frame and bolster. The links have rubber-bonded bushes at each end. The class 83 was the only BR AC locomotive type to have spoked wheels.

Both independent and proportional air brakes are fitted, in addition to train vacuum braking, Davies & Metcalfe equipment being replaced by Westinghouse at refurbishing.

On the EE locomotives the changeover from

Above: The first of the English Electric/Vulcan Foundry built class AL3, later class 83, E3024 on a test run soon after delivery. *(GEC Traction)*

Left: A scene in the erecting shop at Vulcan Foundry, Newton-le-Willows with a batch of class 83 under construction.

    A Transformer conservator tank.
    B Main transformer mounted in the locomotive using the full height of the body interior.
    C Arno convertor for the three-phase auxiliary machines fitted to class 83.
    D Transformer oil cooling fan.
    E Main transformer.
    F Rectifier cooling fan and ducting.
    G Ignitron mercury arc rectifier unit, housing four rectifiers bridge connected to two of the locomotive's traction motors when installed in the locomotive. Two sets were fitted to each locomotive. *(GEC Traction)*

25kV to 6.25kV was achieved by using the main transformer primary winding, which is in four sections; these could be switched from series to parallel connection, according to the supply voltage but in practice did not need to be used.

Fourteen of the EE locomotives had eight ignition liquid-cooled rectifiers each arranged in two groups of bridge connection, each bridge supplying two traction motors in series, with the centre point connected to the transformer, to maintain stable voltage at times of wheel slip. The rectifiers were in two cubicles, each with four sealed ignitrons. The ignitrons were water-cooled units 8in in diameter by 32in high. Each tank had two ignitors, one relieving anode, one energised grid, and of course, the anode and cathode. Stainless steel was used for the vacuum vessel and high-temperature seals used for electrode insulation. The vessel was surrounded by a water jacket for cooling purposes and the cathode block was also water-cooled. Heaters around the anode insulation were designed to stop mercury condensation. Cooling water passed through a fan-cooled radiator by pumping before passing to a distribution manifold containing the water heaters, and on to the rectifiers.

In 1959 it was intended to use mercury-arc rectifiers on 13 locomotives, and silicon on the remaining pair. At one point E3029, the sixth locomotive in the production run, and the fifteenth locomotive, E3305/E3100, were chosen, but only the latter was in fact done.

Locomotive speed control is by on-load tap changing on the transformer secondary winding. Cam-operated contacts are used to select the tappings and electro-pneumatic contactors are used for making/breaking circuits. Weakening of traction motor fields by field-tapping was also employed, whereas all other AC locomotives had divert resistors for field weakening.

The EE type 535A traction motor is a four-pole DC machine of conventional type which, in common with other makers' motors, had its frame modified to accommodate mounting in the bogie frame and the resilient drive. EE used the SLM-BB drive, this having two support arms on the axle side, one solely to carry the motor, the other the SLM-BB stub shaft and gear case. (For description of drive see Chapter 8.) The motors have a continuous rating of 750hp, 837V, 707A, and forced ventilation of 3500 cu ft/min. They operate satisfactorily with a ripple in the current of approximately 30 percent at continuous rating.

The motors have fixed brush gear, the brushboxes having clock-type springs. Braids are fitted on the contact finger of the spring to convey current to the brushbox. The brushes have circumferential stagger, there being three 4-part brushes per brush-arm; one 4-part brush is staggered. One spring for each pair of carbon pieces is fitted; pigtails were not originally fitted to the brushes.

Above: Class 83 bogie of fabricated and rivetted type with conventional axleboxes, but secondary suspension of unusual design.

A Davies & Metcalfe slack adjuster.
B Davies & Metcalfe brake cylinder, maximum operating pressure 50lb/sq in.
C The bolster, a beam passing across the locomotive under the bogie. The locomotive body rests on the bolster through the kingpost and cone, and through to spring-loaded side bearers which in 1978 were undergoing modification.
D Secondary damper.
E Secondary springs, one set each side of the damper.
F APC receiver housing a magnetic switch and reset coil.
G Primary springs and underslung connecting beam to the axlebox.

H Mileometer fitted to the roller-bearing axlebox, which is fitted in conventional horn guides.
J Traction link connecting the bogie to the bolster.
K Secondary suspension hangers connecting the bogie frame top to the spring plank at the bottom, through knife-edge bearings. The spring plank is unusual because it does not pass under the bolster to the hangers on the opposite side of the bogie, but is instead pivoted to the bolster near the bogie centre.
L Axlebox earthing brush connection and cable.
(John Duncan)

Below: Here the type B variant of class 83 is seen at Liverpool Allerton Depot during the period May 1961 to December 1962 when E3304 was converted to type A, and renumbered E3099. *(N. E. Preedy)*

The motor has a lap-wound armature and is equalised at the commutator end for each slot. Twin conductors with glass-braid coverings are cranked to enter the commutator rises. Class H insulation is used on the armature and the field coils. The armature core and commutator are mounted on a common spider pressed on to the shaft.

It is an uncompensated motor with laminated interpoles. The interpole coil is edge-wound to assist heat dissipation and reduce eddy current losses in the conductors. The main field coils are conventional three-tier coils with one tapping for the weak field notches.

Class 83 incorporates surge protection effected by two double rod-gaps, one on the capacitor divider for line surges, and one on the transformer HT bushing for switching surges. A silicon-carbide surge arrestor across each rectifier protected against rectifier ion-starvation. The secondary circuit earth is made through a contactor and a low impedence earth fault relay operating to open the air-blast circuit breaker. The contactor is activated by the same air as the pantograph system, and opens when the pantograph is lowered, which prevents any circulating currents when the locomotive is being towed, and in the case of an earth fault. An interlock on the contactor also opens the ABCB.

Faults in the transformer are detected by a Buchholz relay. Any slow build-up of gas provides a warning, and a sudden build-up of gas causes the ABCB to open. An explosion vent-pipe with a thin gauge copper diaphragm covering the end is arranged to direct ejected oil on to the locomotive roof where it is drained to the ground. Transformer oil temperature is monitored by an over-temperature thermostat which on operation opens the tapping contactors and gives an indication to the driver of a transformer auxiliary fault.

In the event of a motor flashover going to earth, it will trip the overloads and the earth fault relay opens the air-blast breaker, as do rectifier overload relays in the commutating path to protect against back-firing.

The traction motor blowers and the oil-cooling fan motors have no-current proving relays which warn the driver if a motor stops. The warning continues even if the machines are switched-off. Thermostats protect the locomotive water-cooling system.

To cut down station noise — a particular problem with class 83 — auxiliaries can be shut down, so switching-off the blowers and fan. However, should water temperature rises be detected by the thermostat, the auxiliaries are automatically restarted.

The ignitron units required continuous water circulation, and in the event of a loss of power supply, a small DC motor in the water pump was automatically connected to the locomotive battery and maintained water circulation. The 83s, like the 84s, suffered from water-cooled mercury-arc rectifier back-fires. This problem was fortunately controlled by the excellent design of the EE transformer with its surge control characteristics, which limited the surging in the rectifiers, and thus prevented shifting of the windings in the transformer.

The troubles with the rectifiers were intermittent and one could start an 83 from cold, commence a run with a train and the rectifiers would heat up and work without trouble. However, at the end of the run the locomotive would lay over with pantographs down, and on the next run as the rectifiers heated up back-firing would occur. Again, various causes such as mercury condensation, the inability of four rectifiers out of balance to share the load correctly, were quoted as possible causes.

Following experience with E3100 (see Chapter 12), EE and BR discussed in mid-1963 the possibility of fitting the 14 standard 83s with silicon rectifiers and transductor control. Initially, two schemes were proposed:

1. Straight replacement of mercury-arc ignitron rectifiers with silicon semi-conductor rectifiers.
2. As above, but with transductor control and rheostatic brake.

The second scheme would have produced a hybrid design similar to E3100 but without notchless control and weight transfer equipment.

Ideas of other schemes were discussed with BR and three more were added:

3. Fitting an automatic preheating circuit as a standard feature to see if the existing ignitron rectifiers would be improved. No information was put forward to support any improvement by EE.
4. Silicon rectifiers and rheostatic brake.
5. Silicon rectifiers, rheostatic brake, transductor control and smooth tractive effort control.

The idea was again revived in 1967/8, first by

83011 heads the up Hardendale limestone empties
past Willowholme, Carlisle on its journey to Shap in
July 1977.   *(Brian Webb)*

converting E3100 to thyristor control and dual-
braking, in addition to its fitted rheostatic brake;
this scheme was not implemented, either.

The 14 83s were the subject of three more plans.
1. Fitting silicon-diode rectifiers and dual-
   braking.
2. Fitting thyristor rectifiers and dual-
   braking.
3. Fitting thyristor rectifiers, dual-braking
   and rheostatic brake.

In all these programmes equipment was to be
installed internally.

However, yet another scheme came up before
the idea of storing class 83 as surplus to
requirements came about. This involved fitting 14
locomotives with roof-mounted silicon rectifiers
to a BR scheme of January 1968. The idea was that
the rectifiers would be cooled naturally by the air-
flow created as the locomotive moved along. EE
thought the plan likely to be out of gauge. BR
disagreed and was also prepared to risk a degree of
loss of accessibility by mounting the equipment in
a 6ft x 8ft area at No 1 end in the space occupied
originally by the pantograph, the rectifiers being
covered by a radiation screen. A similar scheme
was also in mind for class 84.

AEI, at that time a competitor of EE, had in
mind thyristor conversions for BR too; there was
some urgency as far as EE was concerned,
especially since BR was threatening not to retain
class 83 after the end of 1969 without rectifier
modifications. The idea was again rejected by BR,
but on a cost basis this time, so once again the

straight silicon for ignitron exchange received
consideration, this being the technique finally
chosen, but not until 1972/3.

At this time four motor contactors were added
to protect the silicon rectifiers and isolate traction
motors; the bodyside louvres were converted from
horizontal to vertical to improve cooling air flow
for the new rectifiers; the side corridor centre
window was altered to a louvre because of high
temperatures in the locomotive body, and dual
braking was fitted.

The four-pole traction motors had very thin
brushes of 'wafer' type, glazing of the commutator
occurring due to this form of brush. New brushes
of thicker section have been fitted so that there are
now two wafers per brush, instead of four. The
motors now have good commutation and
reliability.

Their re-introduction into traffic after the
refurbishing programme brought to light again
two problems which were apparent before the
locomotives were stored at Bury. The first was the
high failure rate of the line contactors. These are
the 'tapping' contactors for making/breaking load
currents during 'on-load' tap-changing. Due to
the tap changer operating at traction motor
working voltages, the current being carried by the
line contactors can be very high, hence the type of
contactor specified for this function was the
largest in traction on BR, ie 1500A continuous
rating. In fact, the contactors carry currents up to
3000A for short periods of time during locomotive
acceleration. Predictably this onerous duty has not
been without its accompanying problems.

The design of the contactor has been especially
adapted to allow passage of large continuous

currents by bridging the conventional arcing contacts (for load making/breaking) with a special copper 'bridge' contact block which has two silver contacts for passing the majority of continuous current. From the introduction of class 83, the contactors have been prone to failure by overheating, usually resulting in the contactor burning-up, and often damaging adjacent contactors.

Experience with the locomotives established several reasons for the main silver contacts failing to pass most of the load current. The main problem which still renders the contactor prone to failure is dirt accumulation on the silver contacts. Any loss of current-carrying ability by these main contacts resulted in the copper-braided flexible connector, which carries current to the moving arcing

contact, over-heating sufficiently to ignite the insulated items on the contactor. Severe overheating often resulted in damage to the contactor and adjacent equipment. By eliminating most of the reasons for the bridge contact not conducting current efficiently, the contactor failure rate is now acceptable and non-flammable components are being fitted to eliminate damage should overheating still occur.

The second of the major class 83 problems was weight distribution and its effect on the components of the secondary suspension, or bogie side-bearers. On each side of the bogie is a partial body support arrangement, each of which is designed to carry only 2½ tons of the locomotive body weight. As originally built, the locomotive weight distribution was such that lead ballast was incorporated in several places to spread the weight and prevent the locomotive body leaning when mounted on its bogies. Ballasting was not entirely consistent throughout class 83, but up to refurbishing no problems were encountered with 'body lean'. There were problems with the wear rate of the side-bearer rubbing surfaces, which allow movement of the body with respect to the

Above view of 83007 at Carlisle Kingmoor Depot in 1978, showing the three air reservoirs fitted to classes 81-85 in place of their second pantographs. In this view the centre window glass in the A-side corridor has been replaced by louvres to improve air flow when the class was fitted with silicon rectifiers. *(John Duncan)*

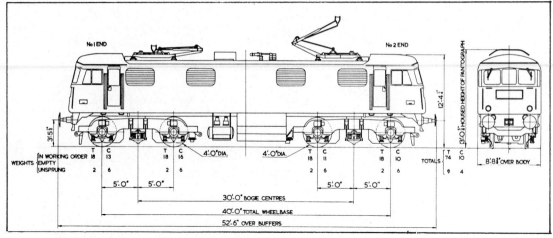

Diagram of class 83 as built when fitted with two
pantographs.   *(British Rail)*

bogies. The rubbing surfaces were originally
manganese liners, but lubrication proved
unsatisfactory, so at refurbishing the surfaces
were modified to stainless-steel rubbing on self-
lubricating PTFE.

Soon after reintroduction into service, the
locomotives were seen to be developing a
significant body lean. On two locomotives this
resulted in arcing from the sides of the pantograph
to signal guards when slowly negotiating quite
severely cambered track bends. It was found that
the weight distribution in class 83 had been
seriously disturbed by removal of some of the
ballast and by replacement of the mercury-arc
rectifier frames. The side-bearer liners were found
to be wearing rapidly due to the lean and to the
small area of the PTFE rubbing disc.

All locomotives needed works attention to
correct the faults. The body lean has been
overcome by suitable attention to secondary
suspension packing according to the amount of
ballast still fitted, and the life of the side-bearer
component satisfactorily extended by increasing
the area of the PTFE rubbing disc.

Class 83 has its transformer mounted inside the
locomotive body with the reactor tank
underneath. It is the only BR AC locomotive type
with transformer secondary tap-changing at
traction motor working voltage. The tapping is off
the secondary transformer at a maximum of 1200V
AC. The tap-changer is driven by a three-cylinder
air motor with oscillating cylinders. The cylinders
are tensioned against nylon discs which can cause

leakage of air when the discs wear away. To give
the facility for retensioning and allowing for wear,
provision was made for shimming discs to be fitted
in the early days. The air motor is extremely
reliable if maintained correctly, which need only
be every four years, compared with the electric DC
motors used on the tap-changers of all other
classes, that need regular attention to brushes etc.

The transformer fan and rectifier fan are
horizontally mounted and have vertical cardan-
shaft drive from a vertically-mounted motor. The
shafts broke at both universal and sliding joints, so
new shafts with resilient mountings (rubber
bushes at each end) were fitted. They can tolerate a
greater degree of inevitable misalignment
between motor and fan impeller.

Some troubles were experienced with excessive
vibration in the traction motor blower fans
because replacement motors were fitted to the old
fan impellers without rebalancing the fans when
mounted on the motors. This is now being carried
out and the problem largely overcome.

The Arno converter on class 83 converts single-
phase AC, supplied from the auxiliary winding of
the main transformer at 415V to AC in three
phases at 415V, supplying five motors. With
water-cooled mercury-arc rectifiers of the
ignitron type, six auxiliary motors were supplied,
the sixth being a water-pump motor, but this
motor was removed when class 83 was fitted with
silicon rectifiers. On the same shaft as the Arno 1-
phase/3-phase converter is a DC generator which
supplies the battery and associated circuits
normally. The Arno single-phase induction motor
is inherently not self-starting because it has no
capacitor start winding like the AC motor on the
other classes; to overcome this the machine is

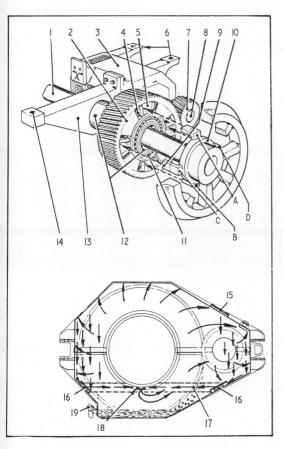

Diagram of Brown-Boveri-SLM drive as fitted in class 83.(Class 84 has the same drive but with a different lubrication system.)

Key: **A, B, C, D,** drive arms.
1 Road wheel axle.
2 Gearwheel mounted on stub arm (13).
3 Traction motor frame.
4 Springs for pads.
5 Spring loaded pads.
6 Mounting points for installation in bogie frame.
7 Traction motor pinion.
8 Pinion shaft.
9 Spider drive arm.
10 Spider directly connected to the axle (1).
11 Roller bearings.
12 Hollow gearwheel support.
13 Stub arm.
14 Mounting points for installation in bogie frame.
15 Inspection plate.
16 Oil catching slot.
17 Oil passage.
18 Oil spout.
19 Oil filler and dipstick.

Motor pinion (7) drives gearwheel (2) which in turn drives resiliently via spring loaded pads (4) the spider (10) through drive arms (9 & A B C D) located inside the locomotive driving wheels   *(GEC Traction)*

rotated to near full speed by connecting the DC generator to the battery and motoring the machine generator. A small tacho-generator on the same shaft detects the correct shaft speed and switches the 415V AC supply to drive the AC motor section of the converter. The DC section of the machine is then switched back to a generator for battery charging.

Three-phase auxiliary machines in class 83 were fitted with miniature circuit breakers, the first application of this in a BR AC locomotive.

Very little trouble has occurred with the BB-SLM drive units which have a slightly different lubrication system, less likely to block up than on class 84 (see Chapter 8), which has an almost identical type of flexible spring drive. One problem which arose before refurbishing was seizure of the gearwheel bearing due to loss of lubricating oil feed from the wicks. The wicks were changed to 100 percent wool, but one more seizure occurred after refurbishing. The problem was identified as contamination of the wicks since they acted as filters, and increased attention to the wicks at depots has totally eliminated this problem.

Two class 83s, E3027/8, returned to VF for extensive repairs following collision damage in February 1965. The locomotives were assessed for costs of the rectification work by EE and in due course the work was authorised by BR. E3028, the worst of the two, had been stripped of its equipment by the end of June. This locomotive had to use a spare bogie to be conveyed to VF as the bogie at No 1 end had been severely damaged. In the repair work the locomotive was cut back to the rear of No 1 cab, the under-frame rebuilt, and a new fabricated drag-box and cab fitted. Much equipment had to be repaired or replaced, and it was ready to return to BR in July 1966. E3027 was less severely damaged, but was affected at both ends and on the 'B' side. Both locomotives were also modified in line with the current BR programme for class 83.

Class 83 was delivered from VF to enter traffic during the period from July 1960, E3024/5 being sent to Longsight in mid-July. The final locomotive, E3100, was used on test work because of its special nature, and although working in early 1962 it was not officially taken into running stock until July.

As deliveries of class 86 locomotives progressed in 1966, classes 83 and 84 were gradually put to one side because of their rectifier failures and cost of

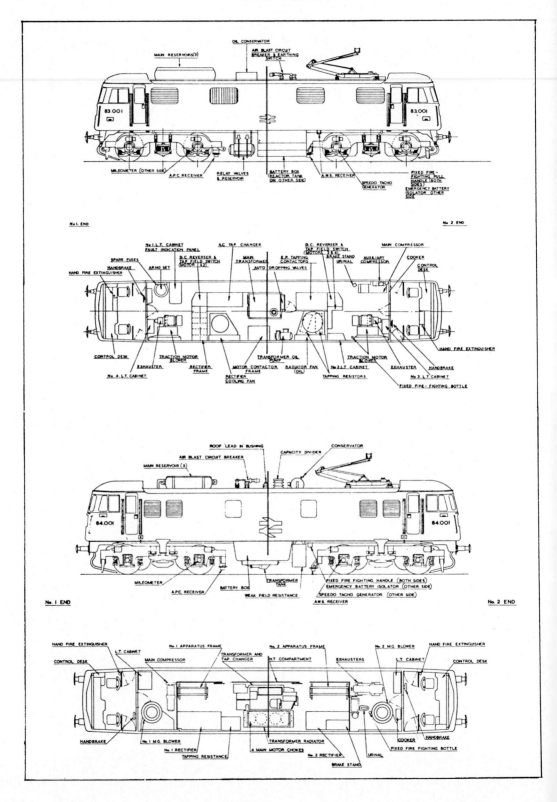

Comparative diagrams of the layout of classes 83 and 84 in 1978.   *(British Rail)*

repair. The non-standard E3100, in spite of being fitted with the successful silicon rectifiers, was stored at Allerton depot, Liverpool, early in 1968. By June some of the others were in store at Longsight, after which they began to gather at Bury shed along with the 84s, for long-term storage. E3100 continued in use for research work, based at Rugby testing station until it too went to Doncaster, following the remainder of the class, in August 1971. The conversion of E3100 to standard was dictated not by its lack of success, but by its being a unique locomotive. Very few drivers knew it and it was not thought a good plan to train more for just one locomotive; for the same reason it was difficult to diagram as a traffic machine, and in fact its running was very restricted.

Refurbishing (the main job being the fitting of silicon rectifiers and dual braking) began when E3034 went to Doncaster in July 1970, and was completed when E3100, converted to a standard locomotive, left the works in October 1973. So far as allocations are concerned, initial deliveries were to Longsight, followed by the general AC lines allocation. The class remained at Longsight in

1978 although some locomotives were lent to Carlisle Kingmoor and Glasgow Shields depot for short crew-training periods before the extension of West Coast main line AC electrification to Glasgow.

Two of the class have been withdrawn. 83003 was involved in the January 1975 Watford accident when it was in collision with 86209 and was withdrawn in May, while the severe damage sustained when 83004 collided head-on with a class 47 diesel locomotive at Willesden resulted in its withdrawal in January 1978. It was cut-up at Willesden and taken to Crewe in sections.

CLASS 83 REFURBISHING DATES (RECTIFIER & DUAL BRAKE CONVERSION)

Loco. No.	Date into Works		Date ex Works	
E3024	June	1972	January	1973
E3025	March	1972	August	1972
E3026	June	1972	January	1973
E3027	November	1971	May	1972
E3028	September	1971	April	1972
E3029	April	1972	August	1972
E3030	June	1972	December	1972
E3031	June	1972	November	1972
E3032	June	1972	February	1972
E3033	June	1971	March	1972
E3034	July	1970	February	1972
E3035	February	1972	July	1972
E3098	July	1971	March	1972
E3099	May	1972	October	1972
E3100	August	1971	October	1973

All refurbished at Doncaster Works

CLASS 83 (AL3) NUMBERING AND CONSTRUCTION DETAILS
Main contractor: English Electric Co Ltd (EE)
Builder of locomotives: Vulcan Foundry Ltd (VF)

Original Number	Subsequent Numbers		EE Works No.	VF Works No.	Date into Traffic
E3024	—	83001	2928	E264	P7/60
E3025	—	83002	2929	E265	P7/60
E3026	—	83003	2930	E266	P8/60
E3027	—	83004	2931	E267	P9/60
E3028	—	83005	2932	E268	P10/60
E3029	—	83006	2933	E269	P10/60
E3030	—	83007	2934	E270	P11/60
E3031	—	83008	2935	E271	P12/60
E3032	—	83009	2936	E272	P12/60
E3033	—	81010	2937	E273	P13/60
E3034	—	83011	2938	E274	P2/61
E3035	—	83012	2941	E277	P7/61
E3303	E3098	83013	2939	E275	P3/61
E3304	E3099	83014	2940	E276	P5/61
E3100	—	83015	2942	E278	P7/62

NOTES

Order Numbers:	EE	— CCH 0916
	VF	— 6794 (E3024-8)
		6795 (E3029-33)
		6796 (E3034/5, E3303/4, E3100)

E3100   Originally allocated number E3305
E3303/4 Renumbered P9/62 and P12/62 respectively when converted from type B to type A locomotives.
83003   Withdrawn 5/75   Watford accident 23/1/75.
83004   Withdrawn 1/78.   Collision at Willesden with Class 47 locomotive 12/77.

CHAPTER 8

CLASS 84 (AL4)

The North British Locomotive Co Ltd (NBL) designed and built the ten class 84 locomotives as sub-contractor to the General Electric Co Ltd (GEC) at its Hyde Park works in Springburn, Glasgow. NBL had been associated with GEC for some years in diesel-electric and electric locomotive contracts for home and overseas.

To meet the specification, NBL decided that a completely integral body structure was necessary, but to employ so far as possible mild steel for all main components. So well was this task accomplished that the finished locomotives were lighter in weight than some competitors' products, incorporating a considerable proportion of lightweight alloy and glass-fibre body components.

The superstructure comprising main frame base and body framing is entirely in 7-gauge mild steel plate; the only exception is in the vicinity of the dragboxes where thickness is increased to ¾in.

The base of the superstructure is a full-width shallow box section of cellular construction, flush on the underside. The sides are curved round and upwards to form the bases for a series of vertical pillars used to form the bodyside frames. At the top, the cant rail is correspondingly curved downwards to meet the pillars. Welding is used to avoid stress concentration. Like the BRCW-Sulzer-AEI 2750bhp diesel-electric locomotive prototype *Lion*, the body structure was a Vierendeel truss.

In the central portion of the width of the frame base, the top decking is raised and the bottom plate lowered to increase the depth of the box section. At the base of the pillars, box-form webs extend between the top deck and the bottom plate. In addition, extra ties and reinforcement longitudinals are included to give an internal cellular construction.

At the ends, members are led up from the base to transfer a proportion of the buffing load to the top of the Vierendeel girder, and at the cab entrance doors, built-up sections are led up and across the roof. At the cab corners, members are led upwards to tie together the cab roof structure, and these provide additional protection to the cab in the event of collisions.

On test, the finished frame of one locomotive was tested in a rig and withstood an end loading of 230 tons. Strain gauges measured no abnormal stresses and the structure was found entirely elastic. The standard test was to 200 tons, as specified for all the BR AC locomotives.

The body is clad externally with cold-rolled full-finish steel sheet welded to the bodyside framework. Windows of half-drop type are placed in the corridor side of the body, but on the equipment side the windows are fixed. The aluminium roof skin on a light steel frame is removable in five sections for maintenance, cabs have a steel frame and skin and the roofs are double-skinned and insulated.

The bogies, of swing-bolster type, have welded box frames fabricated in ⅜in steel plate; the weight of the superstructure is transferred to the bogies through four pillars, two per bogie, which extend from the body to the bogie bolster carrying them. They are located centrally between the bogie wheels but outside the longitudinal centre line of the axlebox journals. The pillars terminate in

Left: The first of the North British Locomotive Co locomotives built for GEC standing alongside the builder's Hyde Park works, Springburn, Glasgow, in early 1960. E3036 of class AL4, later 84.
(Collection of Brian Webb)

Above: View inside the Hyde Park erecting shops showing a class 84 body under construction. The photograph illustrates clearly the all-steel Vierendeel truss form of construction and its great strength especially at the cab doorways, and its light weight.
(Collection of Brian Webb)

spherical steel bearings under which manganese plates are welded. These in turn slide and bear onto manganese pads on the bolsters. Each assembly is enclosed in an oil bath. Between the bogie frame and the bolster are two nests of double helical coil springs, carried on a bracket suspended from the bogie by swing links fitted with rubber-bonded pads.

Hydraulic dampers are used in conjunction with the helical springs, being fixed between the top of the bolster and the swing link brackets. Bogie lateral movement is controlled by rubber pads. Primary suspension comprises coil springs in two nests at the end of each axle, suspended by links with compensating beams resting on rubber pads on top of the axleboxes. The axleboxes have roller bearings by SKF, and manganese liners on the wearing surfaces.

Traction, braking, and transverse forces are taken by a steel centre pin carried in a casting welded to the main frame. The pin terminates in the bogie bolster in a rubber-bonded bush. Forged-steel traction links with rubber bushes take the traction and braking loads to the bogie.

Equipment is similar to that of other types of AC locomotives on BR. The high-tension equipment is fully enclosed behind two inter-locked safety doors; in the centre the main transformer divides the compartment into two halves. On top of the transformer is mounted the supply changeover switch and motor-driven tap changer. Each of the compartments on both sides of the transformer contains one HT equipment frame and one bank of rectifiers with secondary HT gear, arranged symmetrically.

Machinery compartments housing two motor generator traction motor blower sets, two exhausters, main air compressor, auxiliary compressor, LT cubicles etc., are arranged between the HT compartment and the cab bulkheads. The brake equipment frame is in No 2 HT compartment.

GEC 'Com-Pak' type mercury-arc rectifiers took the transformer output via two secondary windings. The rectifiers were arranged so that each pair of traction motors was fed in bridge by four rectifiers from each secondary. These single-anode rectifiers were smaller in size than the conventional mercury-arc types. The 'Com-Pak' rectifier had water cooling. Cathode spot stability with efficient cooling produced high output despite its small size. The arc path was smaller, voltage drop lower, and efficiency higher than conventional types. A feature claimed for the 'Com-Pak' rectifier was its ability to resist vibration and shock, and swilling of the mercury. The cathode spot was anchored.

In class 84 the rectifier equipment was contained in two cases approximately 6ft 0in long by 4ft 6in high, and 2ft 6in deep. The coolant pumps were mounted separately.

Extensive rectifier environment tests were undertaken by GEC on BR tracks using two parcel vans, one housing an 130kW diesel generator set as a power source. The second van carried the transformer, loading resistances and rectifier equipment. Tests included shunting shocks against fixed buffers, runs at 45mph with rapid stops and restarting, runs in loose-coupled goods trains. The equipment was successful, requiring

The withdrawal of a number of class 84 prompted their use on various enthusiasts' specials in 1978; here 84001 climbs rapidly up Beattock with a Locomotive Club of Great Britain train on 17 June 1978.

(Brian Webb)

only minor modification to rectifier mountings. The Hallade recorder was used to record accurately all vertical, horizontal, and canting movements, also acceleration and deceleration. Separate cooling circuits for both anodes and cathodes were used in class 84, optimum temperatures being thermostatically maintained.

The main transformer is oil-cooled by pump circulation through a radiator. The three-limbed core has windings on the outer limbs only, the centre limb acting as a common return path for the magnetic flux. In order to reduce weight the core clamps are extended to form mounting feet to take the core weight. This enables a lightweight oil tank to be employed as it only has to support the weight of the oil.

Cooling for two traction motors and half of the electrical equipment comes from one of the two motor-generator blower sets (MG). These supply air to cool traction motors, smoothing chokes, rectifier, radiators and transformer radiators.

Class 84 bogie. This is probably the best bogie design amongst classes 81-86/0, both for construction and riding quality since modification, having excellent primary and secondary suspension. The bogie frame is of fabricated box frame construction.

A   Body sidebearer. Part of the locomotive body, bearing in a spherical bearing in sliding pads which are immersed in an oil bath. This allows the bogie to swivel. It bears in the bolster, which passes directly across the bogie frame to the sidebearer on the other side of the bogie. The bogie centre king-post passes through the centre and takes traction and braking forces. Traction links connect the bolster to the bogie frame at alternate corners.

B   Secondary suspension hangers from the bogie frame to the spring plank.

C   Primary damper mounted directly on the axlebox.

D   Davies & Metcalfe brake cylinder working at a maximum pressure of 70lb/sq in.

E   Davies & Metcalfe automatic slack adjuster.

F   Flexible sand pipe.

G   Primary coil springs connected across the top of the axlebox by twin beams.

H   Bolster with oil bath.

J   Secondary springs, two sets of coil springs.

K   Spring plank connected to the opposite side of the bogie by a tubular frame. Lateral movement controlled by connecting link to bolster.

L   Secondary dampers.

M   Roller bearing axlebox with earth connection and primary damper bracket.   *(John Duncan)*

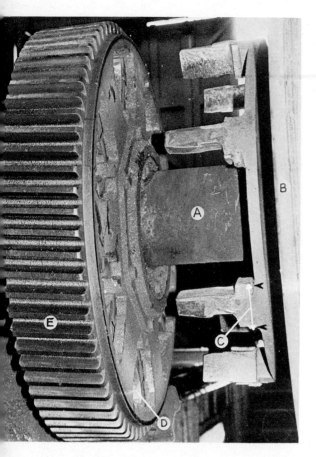

The prime cause of the withdrawal of class 84 has been the failure of the BB-SLM drive arms. Here an example removed from 84001 during the September/October period of 1978 at Kingmoor depot illustrates the problem vividly. The Brown-Boveri drive comprising traction motor stub arm and gearwheel mounted in the stub arm on a roller bearing. The wheels, axle and drive spider show a typical failure with catastrophic wear on the drive arms due to misalignment of the axle in relation to the bogie mounted traction motor, and lubrication deficiencies.

Key: **A** Axle; this passes through the larger clearance of the gearwheel, the gearwheel being bogie mounted. The clearance must be sufficient to allow the wheels and axles to move up and down on the sprung primary suspension.

     B Wheel, showing tyre, tread and flange.

     C One of the drive arms on the main spider wheel connected directly to the axle; the arrows show the original size before wear.

     D Drive plate slot in which coil springs take up the drive inside the gearwheel. It is the oil passage to the base of the slots that blocks due to dirt in the lubricating oil being caught up by the centifugal force set up in the circular oil catcher ring on the opposite side of the gearwheel.

     E Gearwheel driven by the traction motor armature pinion (not shown); the whole assembly is housed in a gearcase.

A revised traction motor/axle alignment has been adopted and gearcases and drives are being thoroughly checked and cleaned, one such check revealing the failure illustrated here.   *(John Duncan)*

Each MG was originally started in sequence from the battery, using the generator as a motor, but were modified to be fed from an auxiliary transformer. Each machine runs up to two-thirds speed before being connected to the AC supply after a preset run-up time. The MG set charging the battery and supplying its associated equipment is voltage-regulated. In event of failure of this MG set, the other set can take over these duties if the relevant MG isolating switch is opened.

The GEC WT501 traction motors are six-pole series-wound force-ventilated machines with compensating windings which have H insulation. Their ratings are: continuous 750hp, 725A, 850V, at 1165rpm; one-hour 890hp, 875A, 850V, at 1100rpm.

The traction motors are mounted through rubber pads in the bogie frame and have fabricated frames to which are bolted the hubs of the BB-SLM spring drives to accommodate the relative movement between motor and axle. The motors are supported in the bogie frame by two brackets on the motor frame and an arm extending from the hub of the BB-SLM drive, forming a three-point mounting. The drive is by a single helical reduction gear with a ratio of 25:74, the large wheel of which is mounted on a quill shaft carried in roller bearings in the drive hub. In the face of the gearwheel a ring of spring-loaded pads engages face dogs integral with a spider pressed on the road wheel hub. The drive is torsionally flexible and free to move vertically inside the quill shaft.

As built, air braking was provided for the locomotive, and vacuum air for the train, using Davies & Metcalfe equipment. Protection for the power equipment in class 84 comprises tripping of the air-blast circuit breaker by current transformer-operated overload relays in the connections to the regulating transformer; an overload relay in the earth end of the rectifier transformer primary circuit, a mid-point earth fault relay and a single-float Buchholz relay. Later secondary overloads were fitted upon conversion to semi-conductor rectifiers. There is also a time delay protecting the tapping resistance and regulating winding against short circuits due to stalling of the tap changer mechanism at a critical position in the switching sequence.

Each traction motor has overload relays to protect against heavy notching overcurrents, and flashovers by a single motor overcurrent relay which arrests the notching sequence on 'run-up' until the traction motor current falls to the designed value with increasing locomotive speed. The tapped section of the regulating transformer has a surge diverter connected across it. Auxiliary equipment (AC and DC) is protected individually by high rupturing capacity (HRC) fuses.

Thermal overload relays and fuses protect the motors of the MG sets, but due to the unreliability of the relay a more discriminating fuse was successfully fitted.

During the 1960-64 period class 84 bogies were poor riders laterally, although vertical ride was considered satisfactory. Secondary damping was moved from between bolster and bogie frame to bolster and spring plank, and the lateral dampers reset. In addition, the snubber rubbers were changed and the swing links altered to locate on knife edge bearings, and new dampers added between bogie frame and axleboxes.

Class 84, in common with class 83, have suffered severe mercury-arc rectifier problems, all of the classes 81-84 having varieties of this type of rectifier until replaced by silicon diodes.

So far as class 84 is concerned, the 'Com-Pak' units were very troublesome in service because of vibrations and continuous service, cooling difficulties and leakages in the cooling circuit. Rectifier imbalance was common, arising from problems in getting loadings aligned in a batch of rectifiers in a locomotive; severe back-firing occurred and repairs were very costly. As early as 1962 E3036 was investigated by GEC at Witton goods depot to see what could be done to improve the situation. The rectifiers had hollow stainless-steel anodes rather than graphite, and in cases of severe back-firing the rectifiers completely failed, often with punctures in the anode unit and loss of vacuum. It was unfortunate too that the class 84 transformers could not withstand the back-firing that resulted in short-circuiting of the windings, which were torn free from their clamps. By late spring of 1963 all ten locomotives were at Dukinfield for modifications, one locomotive E3036 having its transformer strengthened

mechanically, followed by the others. All the faulty transformers were rewound.

From the autumn of 1967 the class was sent for storage in the old steam locomotive depot at Bury, along with class 83. Nine of the class went there, one locomotive, E3043, spending its time at Rugby Testing Station. Their only exercise was at exhibitions of modern rolling stock; in this case E3044 was a common choice. This locomotive visited a number of locations, being noted for example at Bristol Bath Road in October 1968.

The decision to extend the West Coast Main Line electrification from Crewe to Glasgow, and the need to keep costs in check on new motive power, was the salvation for the stored classes 83 and 84. Twenty-five locomotives of these types, plus 35 new locomotives, were considered adequate for this extension. In order to fit classes 83 and 84 for resumption of work, E3042, together with class 83 locomotive, were towed to Doncaster works in July 1970 for examination and a decision on the replacement by silicon of the mercury-arc rectifiers, and other modifications. The programme was initiated in 1971 and the locomotives dealt with by the end of 1972.

A major problem was the electrical flashovers from the high-voltage tap changer 'air make/break' diverter switches to adjacent corridor metal panels. The effect of this electrical arcing was to damage the main transformer windings, from the very high fault currents. Replacing the main transformer and repairing the damaged windings proved expensive.

Attempts to overcome this problem have been made, but continued failures after refurbishing caused the matter to be studied in greater detail by instrumented tests on locomotive 84002 between Longsight and Sandbach in 1974. These tests established the reason for the diverter switch flashovers — the excessively fast speed of operation of the tap changer. The arc extinguishing times of the four associated diverter switches were found to be incompatible with the rate of opening and closing, as determined by the operating speed of the tap changer. Slowing down the tap changer has eliminated the problem of transformer failures, but occasional diverter switch flashovers still occur, though now without damage to other equipment.

The GEC WT501 traction motors gave trouble after refurbishing, although there is no record that this failure had occurred previously. As originally built, the motors had a new type of armature which

One of the now withdrawn examples of class 84,
84006, taking an up parcels train through Tamworth on
20 January 1975.   *(Philip D. Hawkins)*

proved deficient in mechanical winding strength in the critical area behind the commutator. GEC proposals for rectification of this defect were not carried out. The result was insulation breakdown between windings at a pressure point. The time spent stored at Bury was thought to have caused deterioration of the affected insulation. Modifications consisting of reinforcing the affected insulation were put in hand, eliminating these failures.

The motors continued to give poor performance with a high rate of flashover from commutation problems, together with field system insulation faults. In 1974 it was decided that traction motors would need reconditioning. The armatures were rewound to a conventional design and the field systems renovated. Initial experience with the 48 rehabilitated motors (including four spares) was promising, but the failure rate again rose to unacceptably high levels, with electrical faults on both armatures and field systems. At this time failures from collapsed armature bearings also started to occur, possibly from corrosion of the roller bearings at their point of contact during the locomotives' long storage immobile at Bury. The 1976 decision to impose severe restraint on further

expenditure on class 84 was brought about mainly by the poor performance of the traction motors. Some locomotives returned to Doncaster works. 84001/8 were sent there with transformer problems and remained there for over 2½ years, but latterly were awaiting rewound motors, finally returning to service in late 1976.

In 1977/8 the class suffered withdrawals, and it was originally decreed that all would be withdrawn by the end of 1978. The one problem which finally accounted for the first locomotives being withdrawn was severe wear on the flexible spring drive components. The BB-SLM drive, although similar to that on class 83 (which has been relatively trouble free), has on class 84 suffered severe wear on the gearwheel drive arms and the associated spring cups, the shortage of drive arm assemblies causing withdrawal of 84005. Since manufacture of new assemblies was made prohibitive by the financial restraints, locomotives were gradually withdrawn as the drive arms became excessively worn.

Although attempts were made to overcome the wear on the drive components, the cause, thought to be just the lack of lubrication at critical places, has only recently been fully understood.

The BB-SLM drives have six arms in a wheel shape mounted on the axle. The main gear wheel is hollow with six arms and springs fitted each side to allow resilience and axle movement. The gear wheel is mounted in the motor and driven by a pinion. The oil reservoir has wick-type lubricators feeding roller bearings on the gear wheel, and allows oil to drip into the gear case. The oil is picked up by the gear teeth, thus lubricating them, and then flung by centrifugal force to the outer corners of the gear case where two slots catch it. The oil then flows by gravity via an internal channel to a spout inside the gear case which allows the oil to flow into an oil thrower ring on the gear wheel. Centrifugal force impels the oil through passages to lubricate the driving arms.

The cause of the excessive wear of the drive arms is the misalignment of the axle in the vertical plane in relation to the bogie mounted traction motor. When a locomotive bogie is overhauled at Crewe works, the axleboxes are set in the horns so that the bottom of the axlebox is 1in from the horn-stay below the axlebox. The axle loadings are then correctly adjusted, and the traction motor, so that the gear wheel is aligned to the axle. Class 84 locomotives which have had no main works attention since 1976, have their traction motors changed at depots and aligned to main works specification, and the axleboxes to 1in above the top of the horn-stay. With the loss of elasticity in the primary springs since 1976, misalignment results, and the axlebox rests higher in the horns. The drive arms then ride higher in the gear wheel which is attached to the frame-mounted traction motor, wear occurring on the drive arms, and the metallic debris from the wearing process causes lubrication problems.

Collection of foreign matter in the gear case oil galleries and oil-thrower ring have caused oil starvation to the drive arms. This has contributed to the catastrophic drive arm wear, which causes an otherwise useful locomotive to be withdrawn. Special attention is now being paid to topping up the gear case oil level to avoid dry gear teeth and consequential overheating, together with cleaning out all oil-ways.

Withdrawn locomotives are being stripped of components to keep others at work, and it now appears that operating demands will keep the survivors at work as long as possible. In 1978 84001 was in Crewe works during the March-May period receiving two sets of BB-SLM drives

E3036 when new on a test train composed of freight wagons. *(British Rail)*

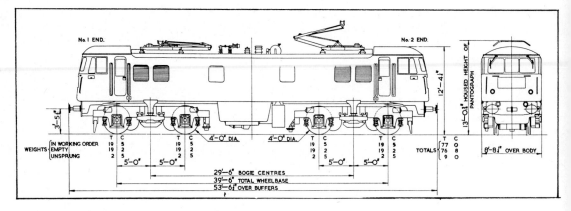

Diagram of class 84 as built with two pantographs.
(British Rail)

from withdrawn 84004. 84001 was partially repainted at Willesden depot for running enthusiasts' specials in the earlier part of 1978. No main works attention was however envisaged in 1978 apart from any casual repairs which could be carried out within financial limits. It is expected that traction maintenance depots should be able to handle most of the work required to keep class 84 in traffic. 84002 was in Crewe works during June–August 1978 being re-tyred and repainted; it also received numbers on all cab sides; the remaining locomotives were being repainted, in view of their poor condition resulting from lack of works attention since 1976.

Delivery of class 84 took twelve months from March 1960. The first locomotive, E3036, was on trial running during January on an energised portion of the Glasgow AC suburban electrification scheme between Singer and Milngavie and was despatched southwards on 8 February.

BR insisted on 'on site' acceptance tests and trials for all its AC locomotives on the LMR. Deliveries progressed slowly, since by October 1960 only E3042 was completed at the NBL Hyde Park Works, with E3043-5 still under way.

They gradually joined locomotives of other manufacturers for crew-training duties on the Styal line, being officially allocated to Longsight depot, but based at East Didsbury until July 1960. They worked various revenue-earning services from September 1960 and when the Manchester-Crewe line was officially opened to electric traction on 12 September 1961, it was class 84 E3040 which worked the inaugural train out of

Manchester Piccadilly station to Crewe.

In 1978 the locomotives were still in remarkably good condition and with very low mileages. Their work is on freight and freightliners at speeds of up to 80mph. This tends to keep mileages low but makes them one of the most heavily loaded types on BR, their work usually being on trains of around 700 tons, mostly in the north of England and into Scotland.

Class 84 was probably the best-looking and best-finished of the initial AC locomotive designs, while its design and construction by a traditional locomotive builder using traditional materials, notably in the bogie work, has resulted in a good-riding and popular locomotive.

Transformer cooling radiator leakages in 84009 resulting in oil contamination of other locomotive equipment was brought to a head in July 1978. Although the class was approved for continuation in service until 1982, with no main works heavy expenditure allowed, it was decided that as 84003 had just been found to have ⅝in wear on its BB-SLM drive arms because of inadequate lubrication, a good locomotive could be made out of the pair by the expedient of exchanging bogies, allowing 84009 to be withdrawn. The exchange was undertaken at Carlisle Kingmoor depot which has considerable faith in class 84. Kingmoor depot has carried out special work on class 84 in recent times due to the relatively heavy workload at the owning depot, Crewe. Kingmoor retains an active interest in class 84 by doing any necessary heavy lifting work to assist Crewe depot.

84009 was not scrapped, being converted at Derby into a research vehicle for use in test programmes to eliminate interference caused by AC traction and thyristor-equipped traction units (see Chapter 12). Its use as a mobile load-bank by the Chief Signal & Telecommunications Engineer, and by the Chief Mechanical & Electrical Engineer on systems tests and overhead wire energisation tests provided a means of drawing a constant overhead wire current while being hauled through 25kV feeding sections to signal boxes. Upon conversion, the locomotive had its No 2 MG set, vacuum exhauster, vacuum brake frame, and traction motor cabling taken out. The traction motor carcasses were loaded up with ballast, and three sets of dynamic brake, brake resistors, associated fans and framework, ducting, etc, were fitted. The body was modified with additional louvres to provide air inlet and exhaust for cooling items of new equipment. Some recabling and new instrumentation was fitted.

Drive arm wear was again found on 84003 in December 1978. With no spare arms in stock, there were hopes that the unmachined drive arms at BREL Crewe would be made ready, but this was not to be. Meanwhile the National Railway Museum decided to preserve 84001 as a static exhibit, thus permitting its wheel sets to be salvaged for 84003 and any others in the near future which may require them.

Late in 1978 GECT was seeking to purchase one of the remaining class 84s for use as an experimental locomotive in connection with regenerative braking development for AC traction. In its re-equipped form the locomotive would be thyristor-controlled and undergo trials on BR, in addition to being made available to BR for operation of traffic.

On 29 April 1978 84001 worked an enthusiasts' special from Euston to Crewe and return, running successfully for long distances at around 100mph. The ride is very good at 100mph and liked by drivers, but low reliability brought about the recommendation to the operating department to avoid their use on Class 1 passenger trains, except for enthusiasts' specials upon request; they are however seen at times on passenger duties.

On 17 June 1978 a further special from Liverpool to Crianlarich with 84001 was organised by The Locomotive Club of Great Britain. 84001 topped Beattock at 70mph, in spite of a check to 30mph at Greskine, with a 13-coach load of 455 tons! 84001 worked only on the section from Preston to Glasgow and back, the train being otherwise diesel-hauled.

CLASS 84 (AL4) NUMBERING AND CONSTRUCTION DETAILS

Main contractor: General Electric Co Ltd (GEC)
Builder of locomotives: North British Locomotive Co Ltd (NBL)

Original Number	New Number	NBL Works No	Date into Traffic
E3036	84001	27793	P3/60
E3037	84002	27794	P5/60
E3038	84003	27795	P6/60
E3039	84004	27796	P7/60
E3040	84005	27797	P8/60
E3041	84006	27798	P10/60
E3042	84007	27799	P10/60
E3043	84008	27800	P12/60
E3044	84009	27801	P13/60
E3045	84010	27802	P3/61

NOTES

Locomotives built under NBL order No L91 of 18 February 1957.

84001   Withdrawn 22/1/79 for preservation.
84004   Withdrawn 12/11/77. BB-SLM drive arms worn, and split bellows ducting.
84005   Withdrawn 20/4/77. Collision damage at Stafford, and subsequent shortage of BB-SLM drive arms for wheel sets.
84006   Withdrawn 20/4/77. Worn tyres and wear on two BB-SLM drive arms.
84007   Withdrawn 10/1/78. BB-SLM drive arms worn. Transformer problems.
84009   Withdrawn 3/8/78. BB-SLM drive arms worn.

CLASS 84

REFURBISHING PROGRAMME (RECTIFIER & DUAL BRAKE CONVERSION)

Loco No	Date into Works		Date ex Works	
E3036	May	1972	December	1972
E3037	March	1971	September	1972
E3038	March	1971	May	1972
E3039	March	1971	June	1972
E3040	November	1971	July	1972
E3041	March	1972	October	1972
E3042	July	1970	May	1972
E3043	March	1971	August	1972
E3044	April	1972	November	1972
E3045	February	1972	October	1972

All refurbished at Doncaster Works

CHAPTER 9

CLASS 85 (AL5)

Forty sets of equipment were ordered by BR for use in locomotives built in its own workshops. The equipment is generally similar to that used in class 81, the AEI (BTH) locomotives. The principal variation is that the BR Doncaster-built locomotives had semi-conductor rectifiers and rheostatic braking. Thirty locomotives (E3056-85) were built with germanium rectifiers, and then with silicon rectifiers (E3086-95). The locomotives were designed at Doncaster and were very similar to those produced by industry, being built to the same specification. Originally it was intended to divide the order for building between Doncaster and Crewe.

The locomotive underframe is an assembly welded up from seven steel box-sections — drag box and cabs, bogie centres, intermediate sections and transformer well section. The vertical lateral and longitudinal members are 5/16in steel plate, and the top and bottom plates 3/8in thick. The frame takes the buffing and drawgear loadings.

The superstructure design required lightness and was original in concept. The lower halves of the bodysides and the underframe are joined to form a deep trough section. The panels are of 5/16in steel plate, flanged at the top to give stiffness and provide seatings for the roof unit. The upper half of the locomotive body to waist level is based on a lightweight welded-steel frame clad with riveted aluminium panels. Aluminium roof traps are also fitted to facilitate access to equipment. The whole of the top half of the body between the cab bulkheads is removable as one unit. The idea was developed from French railways' work. Driving cabs are of double-skin steel construction based on a steel frame; up to window level the cab sides are integral with the main frame structure. The cab front is of flanged plates to give maximum stiffness.

The bogies are of underslung equalising beam type, the beams being carried from the Timken roller-bearing axle-boxes on combined shear and compression rubber pads. The bogie frame is an assembly of rolled-steel channel side members welded to form box-sections, and also fabricated transoms and headstocks. Four double-coil helical

springs support the bogie frame on the equalising beams.

As in class 81, Alsthom rubber cone pivots are fitted, as also are radius arm guided axleboxes. The body is carried mainly on the rubber cone pivots on each bogie, but four spring-loaded side bearers are also fitted.

The main transformer of class 85 was changed slightly when it was decided to fit semi-conductor rectifiers. However, modifications were small, as it was desirable to retain the transformer in almost original form. The windings were altered from bi-phase (ie for class 81) to take account of the bridge rectifier circuits, the ratings becoming:
Secondary fixed voltage winding 6.25V 1810 KVA
Secondary tapped winding 9 × 234V 1730 KVA
2110/578V 1700 KVA

Tap changing is similar to class 81, but the lower half of the control frame was modified to take account of the differing traction motor circuits. This part of the frame carries the reverser and power brake changeover switches in the DC side of the excitation circuits. Isolation of motors is obtained by control of motor contractors, whereas class 81 has a motor cut-out switch with power contacts in each motor circuit.

The use of semi-conductors removed the need for high-speed line breakers; their space was used to accommodate the contactor frame carrying eight motor contactors, the field shunting contactors and a DC excitation contactor for the braking circuits as rheostatic braking was incorporated on class 85.

The semi-conductor rectifier is built up with strings of cells mounted in vertical trays. The germanium locomotives have 20 trays, the silicon locomotives 12 trays, each containing 64 and 28 cells respectively. The trays are arranged to slide out of the frame into the corridor for inspection purposes. The cells are in series and the strings connected in parallel groups to form the arms of a bridge circuit. Each tray had four protecting fuses and the locomotive could operate normally with one string of cells cut-out. This was later replaced by secondary overload relays. Cooling is by axial cooling fans.

A pair of new class AL5, later class 85, locomotives on a
test train, E3057 leading.   *(GEC Traction)*

Class 85 has eight line contactors on the motor
circuit instead of the two large high-speed line
contactors used on class 81. This alteration was
due to the fitting of semi-conductor rectifiers in
class 85. The basic principles are that as the
locomotive slows, the train weight pushes against
the locomotive, the locomotive wheels then begin
to drive the traction motors. The motors become
generators because of the propelling force, and the
armatures produce electric power which is
dissipated as heat in resistors. The electric power
generated is also used to drive a cooling fan, which
in turn cools the resistors. A partial friction brake
application on the train helps to stop jolts as the
train closes on the locomotive, and to stop
'snakings' on slack couplings.

The traction motor field coils are supplied from
the main transformer via an excitation
transformer, and the tap changers control the
output which is no longer controlled by the
driver's notching handle but the driver's
automatic brake valve.

The driver applies the automatic brake valve in
the locomotive cab to slow or stop the locomotive
and train. A small control switch is made in the
brake valve to set the traction motor circuits for
braking, while at the same time the locomotive and

train brakes apply in the normal way. When
sufficient electric power has been generated by the
traction motors, it is sensed by the locomotive's
control circuit. The locomotive brakes are slowly
released automatically until the pressure in the
brake cylinders reaches 10lb/sq in, which is just
enough to keep the brake blocks rubbing on the
wheels.

The generating traction motors are controlled
by the reducing air pressure in the train pipe. This
is done by the driver's brake valve. The drop in air
pressure operates the locomotive and train friction
brakes, an actuator (air to electric control valve)
runs-up the tap changer, thereby increasing the
electric current through the traction motor field
coils. This increases the magnetism across the
traction motor armatures, slowing down the
traction motor armatures, the locomotive and
train wheels.

Rheostatic braking, sometimes referred to as
'dynamic' braking, was not in general use on class
85 in 1978 but was on all class 86/87 locomotives.
It saves an enormous amount of wear on
locomotive brake blocks, reduces locomotive time
out of traffic, and the braking effort is smoother
than friction brakes. E3067 was the first class 85
equipped with automatic rheostatic braking,

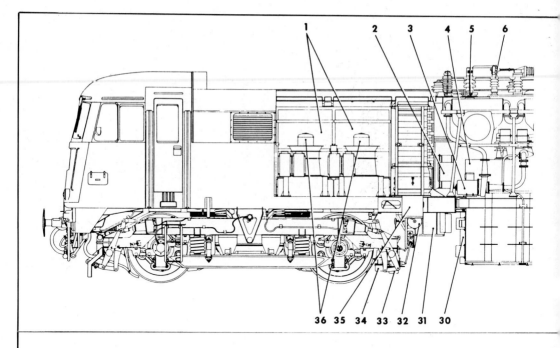

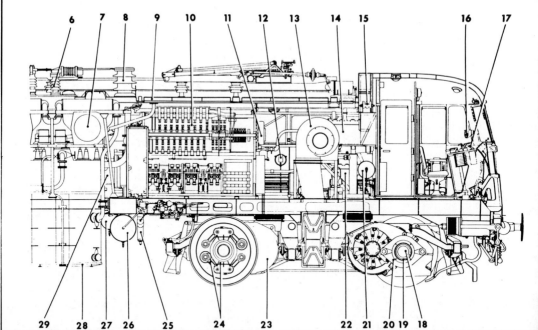

being undertaken in conjunction with AEI and the Westinghouse Brake & Signal Co Ltd. The conversion was done in 1964.

Class 85 originally had a power/brake selector switch in the cab, and the driver used the notching handle to control the amount of rheostatic brake. This method was not generally favoured by drivers and if not correctly used produced severe braking jolts in the train. To overcome the lack of use, and the problems due to mishandling it was decided to make the rheostatic braking system automatic in action. This was achieved by operating it through, and in conjunction with, the locomotive automatic brake valve.

Equipment layout diagram of class 85.

Key:

1	Rectifier frame.	**19**	Hollow driving quill.
2	Braking excitation equipment.	**20**	Driving flange pin.
3	Transformer oil-circulating pump.	**21**	AWS vacuum reservoir.
4	Main transformer.	**22**	No 2 exhauster.
5	Roof through-bushing.	**23**	Traction motor.
6	Air blast circuit breaker.	**24**	Driving spreader and connecting links.
7	Transformer cooling fans.	**25**	Air drier.
8	Roof capacitor.	**26**	Brake supply reservoir.
9	Conservator tank.	**27**	Control air reservoir.
10	Main control unit.	**28**	Main transformer.
11	Geneva gearbox.	**29**	Auxiliary transformer.
12	Vacuum governor.	**30**	DC smoothing choke.
13	Traction motor blower.	**31**	Battery charger saturable reactor.
14	No 1 exhauster.	**32**	Vacuum reservoir.
15	Exhauster field divert resistor.	**33**	AWS receiver.
16	AWS indicator.	**34**	APC receiver.
17	Power brake switch.	**35**	Braking resistor fan.
18	Axle.	**36**	Rectifier cooling fans.

On class 85 a small excitation transformer between the main transformer and the traction motor fields is used, as the tapping direct from the main transformer proved too much for the small amount of current required by the traction motor field while braking. Classes 86 and 87 do not have an excitation transformer; a main transformer secondary winding is used, ie that for No 4 traction motor. This is achieved by using four decompounding resistors in series with each field on the four traction motors. The decompounding resistors are shared with the current flowing through the braking circuit. The decompounding resistors have the effect of keeping the braking effort higher at lower speeds, giving the rheostatic brake a greater braking range.

In 1978 only 85007 had working rheostatic brake due to several problems, but general reinstatement was in hand, and in late 1978 plans were being made to bring the rheostatic brake into use on all class 85 locomotives. Class 86 resistor banks may have to be fitted in place of the existing equipment which is not in good condition after so long a period of disuse.

All the 85s with germanium rectifiers were converted to silicon rectifiers, to become standard with the E3086-95 batch, so fitted when built. E3056-60/2/8-85 were fitted with AEI silicon rectifiers, and E3061/3-5 with Westinghouse silicon rectifiers during the 1968-71 period.

E3073 was used in high-speed tests on the Crewe-Stafford section in 1963/4, up to 119mph being reached to test the overhead wire equipment, which was of new design. With one of its twin pantographs instrumented, E3073 was coupled to the test vehicle, known as the 'gondola car' which is a bogie vehicle, having a flat roof with a central observation portion, and now known as *Test Car Mentor*. It carried a Hallade recorder which checked for excessive movement. Runs were made with a generator car and *Mentor*, giving an 85-ton tail load, and with Mentor plus one brake second carriage, giving a 65-ton load.

The class 85 protection system is similar to that of class 81 except for the rectifiers. The AEI type 189 six-pole traction motor has experienced similar troubles to the idential motor fitted on classes 81 and 82. In earlier class 85 locomotives drivers reported banging noises in the bogies, which were found to be due at times to the axleboxes banging on the bogie frames. This was tested by the simple expedient of sticking blobs of chewing gum on the axlebox tops and observing it in a flattened state after running. The rough riding problems with the Alsthom type suspension on the class 85 bogies were similar to those experienced with class 81, and the results of the tests set out in Chapter 5 were found suitable for class 85 too, with the result that extra primary damping was being considered for class 85.

Class 85 and class 81 have in recent years experienced severe wear in their Alsthom drive units. The rubber bushes in the links began to wear so that the drive arm crank pins were found to be hitting the location holes in the locomotive wheels, in some cases causing elongation of the holes which resulted in wheel sets having to be changed. One 85 locomotive was built for test purposes with axle-hung traction motors and without the Alsthom drive, normal reduction gearing pinions being used for the drive. The locomotive was subsequently converted to standard.

The 40 Doncaster-built locomotives of class 85 were delivered between June 1961 and the end of

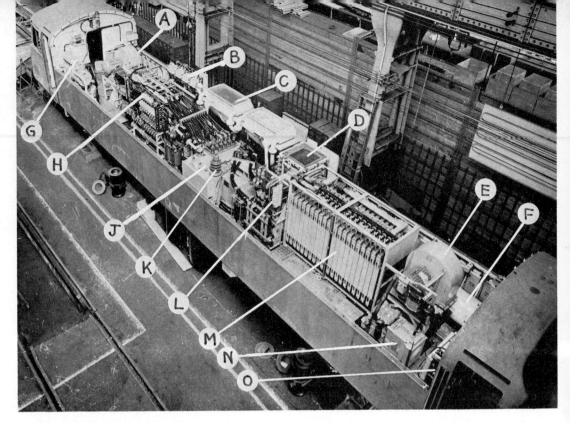

A class 85 locomotive of the germanium rectifier batch E3056-85 under construction at the BR works, Doncaster. The body is complete with cabs and lower bodysides; the top bodysides and roof units have still to be fitted.

A   No 2 traction motor blower which forces cooling air from the bodyside louvres to Nos 3 and 4 traction motors.

B   Field divert contactors. The line contactors are mounted underneath.

C   Transformer oil-cooling radiators. Two fans below force air through the radiators and through the louvred roof ducting.

D   Rheostatic brake resistor bank cooled by air from a cooling fan mounted beneath the locomotive floor.

E   No 1 traction motor blower cooling Nos 1 and 2 traction motors.

F   Main air reservoir, now mounted as three reservoirs on the locomotive roof.

G   Vacuum exhauster; a second exhauster is mounted underneath.

H   Main control unit housing the tap changer. Note the cables from the secondary terminals on the main transformer to the tap changer.

J   Main transformer.

K   25000V input connection and insulator to main transformer.

L   Control equipment for switching in the excitation transformer for rheostatic braking.

M   Main rectifier trays, twenty trays housing a total of 1036 germanium semiconductor diodes; an arrangement of diodes is termed a rectifier.

N   Main air compressor, now mounted behind the traction motor blower (E).

O   Fault indicator panel containing fault indicator lights and flag, also control circuit fuses.

(British Rail)

1964. E3056 was under construction in spring 1960, being noted completed in early November 1960, but none was officially into traffic until June 1961, being allocated to Crewe depot. By September 1962 some locomotives were stored in the sidings at Goostrey due to shortage of work for them at the time. After a spell allocated to LMR AC lines, in 1978 all class 85 was allocated to Crewe depot. In 1974 some moved up to Glasgow Shields depot for a short stay on crew-training duties.

The class 85 work mainly on freight trains and on the overnight Anglo-Scottish passenger trains on the same diagrams as classes 81-83. Classes 81-85 cannot haul air-conditioned trains because they are not fitted with the same earthing arrangement as classes 86 and 87.

The original classes of BR AC locomotives are being considered for a major refurbishing programme in the near future, although classes 81, 82, 83 and 85 alone are to be done, leaving out the survivors of class 84. It is apparent from this that withdrawal of the early classes is unlikely in the foreseeable future.

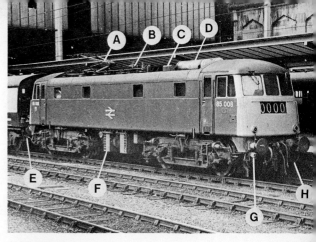

85008 at Carlisle in August 1978 showing all the modifications visible externally, and other features.

Key: **A** Stone-Faiveley AMBR pantograph fitted with automatic dropping device.

B Brown-Boveri air blast circuit breaker.

C Louvred duct providing an outlet for the hot air being blown from the rheostatic brake resistor bank.

D The three main air reservoirs fitted to give increased capacity and higher pressures (140lb/sq in) for hauling airbraked trains.

E Electric train heat cable on the locomotive plugged into socket on the first coach. On the opposite side the cable on the coach will be plugged into the socket on the locomotive.

F Two modified smoothing chokes, smaller than the original, but forced-air cooled by a double rotor fan motor mounted longitudinally between the two chokes.

G Electric train heat socket.

H Electric train heat cable and plug fitted in dummy socket to complete the 110V proving circuit.

(John Duncan)

CLASSES 81-85
AUXILIARY MACHINE DRIVING MOTORS

Function of Motor	Number of Motors per Locomotive Class				
	81	82	83	84	85
Traction motor blowers	2	4	2	–	2
Main air compressor	1	1	1	1	1
Auxiliary air compressor	1	1	1	1	1
Vacuum exhauster	1	(0)1	1	1	1
Battery driven exhauster	1	1	1	1	1
Transformer oil pump	1	1	1	1	1
Rectifier fans	(3)2	(3)2	1	-	1
Rectifier intake fan	-	(1)-	-	-	-
Rectifier coolant pump	-	-	(1)-	(4)-	-
Smoothing reactor fan	1	-	-	-	1
Arno converter	-	-	1	-	-
Motor generator/blowers	-	-	-	2	-
Camshaft motor	1	1	1(Air)	1	1
Rheostatic brake fan	-	-	-	-	1
Battery charger	1	-	-	-	1
DC generator	-	1	1	1	-
Emergency water pump	-	-	(1)-	-	-
Oil cooler fan	2	1	1	-	2

NOTE

Numbers in brackets give the original figure.

Diagram of class 85 as built with two pantographs.
(British Rail)

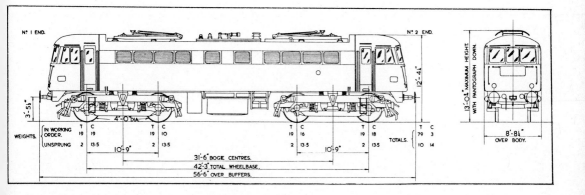

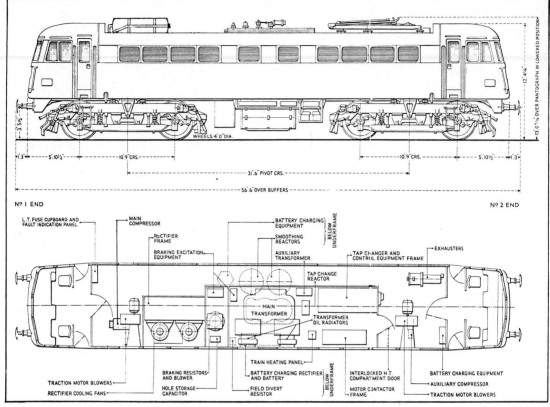

Diagram and equipment layout of class 85 as running in 1978.
(British Rail)

CLASS 85 (AL5) NUMBERING AND CONSTRUCTION DETAILS

Traction equipment contractor: Associated Electrical Industries (BTH)

Builder of locomotives: BR Doncaster

Original Numbers	New Numbers	Date into Traffic
E3056	85001	P9/61
E3057	85002	P6/61
E3058	85003	P6/61
E3059	85004	P8/61
E3060	85005	P8/61
E3061	85006	P13/61
E3062	85007	P13/61
E3063	85008	P11/61
E3064	85009	P12/61
E3065	85010	P12/61
E3066	85011	P4/62
E3067	85012	P1/62
E3068	85013	P5/62
E3069	85014	P5/62
E3070	85015	P8/62
E3071	85016	P11/62

Original Numbers	New Numbers	Date into Traffic
E3072	85017	P12/62
E3073	85018	P2/63
E3074	85019	P13/62
E3075	85020	P1/63
E3076	85021	P4/63
E3077	85022	P3/63
E3078	85023	P3/63
E3079	85024	P10/63
E3080	85025	P4/63
E3081	85026	P7/63
E3082	85027	P6/63
E3083	85028	P9/63
E3084	85029	P5/64
E3085	85030	P7/64
E3086	85031	P3/62
E3087	85032	P11/62
E3088	85033	P2/63
E3089	85034	P7/63
E3090	85035	P11/63
E3091	85036	P10/63
E3092	85037	P2/64
E3093	85038	P11/63
E3094	85039	P2/64
E3095	85040	P13/64

BR Doncaster Order Numbers: E016 (E3056-65)
                                     E017 (E3066-74)
                                     E019 (E3075-95)

CHAPTER 10

CLASS 86 (AL6)

Following experience with the first hundred AC locomotives, BR ordered the same number of second-generation locomotives all of which it classified AL6, and later 86.

The locomotives were fitted with traction equipment supplied jointly by EE and AEI. AEI supplied the traction motors, tap changers, many of the auxiliary machines, rheostatic brake equipment and the cabling; EE supplied all the rectifiers, transformers, control gear, wheelslip protection equipment, and some auxiliary machines.

The mechanical design was undertaken by BR at Doncaster and the manufacture and erection of the locomotives divided between BR Doncaster and the EE Vulcan Foundry at Newton-le-Willows, initially 60 and 40 locomotives, subsequently altered to 40 and 60 respectively.

The mechanical portion comprises a super-structure similar to that of class 85, while the bogies and primary and secondary suspension are also similar. The design was based on previous experience and was an advance, notably in interior layout to aid maintenance, although this was certainly helped by the locomotives being 2ft 0in longer compared with class 85, while the reduced wheel diameter gave more interior height and headroom.

Like class 85, the whole of the upper half of the equipment compartment is arranged for complete removal between the cabs. The most noticeable difference externally is in the shape of the cab front, which was given a flat lower half in contrast with the rearward-sloping front of classes 81 to 85. Although this was said to improve the appearance, the substitution of a slow shape for a fast shape makes this a matter of opinion.

The fitting of only one pantograph — 90 locomotives with Stone-Faiveley, and 10 with the AEI crossed-arm type — was the result of experience gained on classes 81 to 85. A Brown-Boveri air-blast circuit breaker is mounted on the roof but no voltage sensing device is fitted, as the 86 is not designed to operate on 6.25kV. The pantograph is located at No 2 end, in line with classes 81-85, although originally intended for No 1 end on class 86.

Equipment layout has been revised in comparison with class 85. The transformer, with HT tap changer, conservator, oil radiators, oil pump and pipework as a complete unit, is mounted centrally in a well in the underframe. The two rheostatic brake units are placed one at each end of the transformer, working with the nearest traction motors. Main rectifiers are placed one in each corner of the locomotive body, each supplying one traction motor. A traction motor blower and smoothing inductor is mounted below each rectifier, and each blower draws its air supply over the rectifier cooling fins and through the inductor before supplying it to the traction motors. Each of four separate transformer secondary circuits feeds one traction motor through a silicon rectifier bridge. The traction motors have one field strength only, simplifying control. Transformer tap voltage is varied by an HT tap changer with 38 running notches, and although provision is made for two weak field notches, it is not used.

The traction motors are four-pole 900hp units without field weakening; these motors are unusual for BR AC locomotive practice in being nose-suspended, with roller-bearing axle suspension. Resilient gears are used. Recourse to axle-hung motors, rather than the flexible drive as used in the 100 initial AC locomotives, was due to experience in diesel-electric main line locomotives with this type of motor, and the fact that it is less complex and expensive. Experience has shown this was a mistake for locomotives operating up to 100mph, and was modified in class 87, and indeed modifications were made with class 86, as will be seen later. Two varieties of the AEI 282 traction motor are fitted. Although these vary in power, they are interchangeable. The 282 AZ motor has a full field power rating of 3600hp and the 282 BZ motor 4040hp, at four motors per locomotive.

Rheostatic braking up to 2000kW is provided, each traction motor armature having a braking resistance connected across it. During dynamic

braking the fields of all motors are connected in series and supplied with current from the transformer windings and associated rectifier bridge for No 4 traction motor. Two brake valves are provided in each cab; one is the normal Westinghouse straight air brake for the locomotive only; the automatic brake valve controls the locomotive brakes (air and rheostatic) and the train brakes (air or vacuum).

The fitting of a single automatic brake handle to perform all functions was new to BR. It is arranged to control the air pressure in the air brake pipe, a reduction in this pressure serving to apply all brakes in proportion — air, vacuum and electric.

As the electric brake is slow coming into action, the air brake is applied first, and automatically reduced to a nominal 10lb/sq in as soon as the electric brake has built up to a preset value. Thereafter, the locomotive air brake stays at 10lb/sq in to keep the brake rigging taut but the electric brake can be increased automatically in proportion to the train brake application, up to the limit of motor braking performance.

Wheelslip protection was not specified for class 86. However, wheelslip with motor over-speeding occurred in some circumstances of load, speed, and low adhesion. This was confirmed by tests, with the result that the class was fitted with

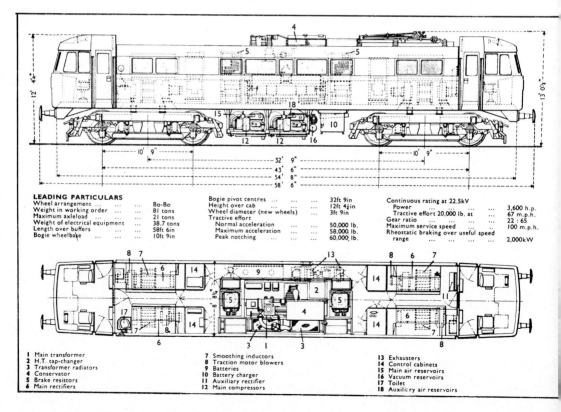

LEADING PARTICULARS

Wheel arrangement	Bo-Bo	Bogie pivot centres	32ft 9in		Continuous rating at 22.5kV	
Weight in working order	81 tons	Height over cab	12ft 4½in		Power	3,600 h.p.
Maximum axleload	21 tons	Wheel diameter (new wheels)	3ft 9in		Tractive effort 20,000 lb. at	67 m.p.h.
Weight of electrical equipment	38.7 tons	Tractive effort			Gear ratio	22 : 65
Length over buffers	58ft 6in	Normal acceleration	50,000 lb.		Maximum service speed	100 m.p.h.
Bogie wheelbase	10ft 9in	Maximum acceleration	58,000 lb.		Rheostatic braking over useful speed	
		Peak notching	60,000 lb.		range	2,000 kW

1 Main transformer	7 Smoothing inductors
2 H.T. tap-changer	8 Traction motor blowers
3 Transformer radiators	9 Batteries
4 Conservator	10 Battery charger
5 Brake resistors	11 Auxiliary rectifier
6 Main rectifiers	12 Main compressors

13 Exhausters	
14 Control cabinets	
15 Main air reservoirs	
16 Vacuum reservoirs	
17 Toilet	
18 Auxiliary air reservoirs	

wheelslip detection and automatic correction equipment of EE design. These tests were carried out with locomotive E3161 which was fitted with water spraying equipment to simulate wheelslip conditions. Protective devices in classes 86 and 87 involved a large-scale use of miniature circuit breakers (MCB) for ease in fault-finding. An early problem was the slipping of traction motor pinions. Locomotives in service were modified, and those under construction dealt with as built. The modification involved the fitting of a pinion retaining plate.

Class 86 proved more reliable and easier to maintain than classes 81-85. Nevertheless problems encountered with bogies and the rough riding of the class 86 locomotives brought many complaints from crews, while its effect on the locomotive equipment was not satisfactory. The riding problems were apparent mostly in the vertical plane.

Locomotive riding is measured by a mean ride index, which bases the riding quality by a frequency of body oscillations. The class 86 was found to have a mean ride value index of 4, and the following indicates how the index is put into practical terms:

Mean ride index	Description
1.0	Very good
2.0	Good
3.0	Satisfactory
4.0	Acceptable
5.0	Dangerous

The hydraulic damping on the primary suspension of class 86 was partly responsible for the problem, and experience revealed that the systems employed on classes 81-85 were not suitable for sustained riding qualities at high speeds. Dampers with symmetrical characteristics in bump and rebound were required, and in 1968 tests were undertaken with damping of this nature; they demonstrated that riding qualities had been improved both in vertical and lateral planes. Further improvements were possible in the primary suspension, but the secondary suspension was the next problem. It was found that the secondary would have to be modified to reduce the ride index to within the 3.5 to 3.75 area, both in vertical and lateral planes at the high speeds class 86 were to do.

The existing bogie was found to have limited possibilities, and a design study was instigated in May 1968. The class 86 bogie, similar to that of classes 81 and 85, had the Alsthom suspension.

This involves the double rubber cone to take about half the body weight at each bogie, and the rest of the weight was taken by four spring pads on each bogie's side members. The static deflection in this suspension is limited to about 1½in but due to the hysteresis of the rubber cone unit, the dynamic characteristic became equivalent to a more rigid assembly. It was decided that attempts to improve riding in the vertical plane must result in a softer suspension, but must not adversely affect the locomotive roll or sway characteristics, to avoid lateral displacement at the pantograph overhead wire level.

In Germany, the Federal Railway's electric locomotives of class 103 were running at 125mph with a secondary suspension using helical springs to deal with vertical, lateral, and bogie rotational displacements; this system termed 'flexicoil' was considered by BR and investigations aimed at a static deflection of 3¼in resulted in class 86 E3173 being fitted with a flexicoil secondary suspension at Crewe works in May 1969. Twelve coil springs mounted outboard of the bogie sideframes were fitted at each corner in groups of three. They supported the whole of the body weight, body displacement being checked by hydraulic dampers. A traction pad assembly in each bogie transmitted traction and braking forces. Tests with E3173, or *Zebedee* as it was affectionately nicknamed (after the BBC television 'Magic Roundabout' cartoon character), indicated that use of the secondary suspension would not benefit the forces taken by the track, as the bogie unsprung weight would still remain a problem. E3173 completed its tests and entered normal service in September 1969.

While work on design and testing of E3173 proceeded, class 86 bogie side frames began to fracture in the fillet welds on the tension side of the transom to side frame connection. They were found to be fatigue fractures and the fault was so common throughout the class that it caused the 'shopping' of seven locomotives per week for attention at Crewe locomotive works.

The fractures were treated with a needle descaling pistol that contains flat rather than pointed needles which under 90lb/sq in pneumatic operation bombard the surface; care was taken to achieve a standardised process. The process produced compression stressing in the surface of the weld and the weld toes, so raising the stress limits and increasing the life of the welded joint. After two years the bogie frames fractured

again; this time it was a major fault in the bogie side frame at a different place. A similar process to the treatment previous was adopted and all class 86 passed through Crewe works, being finished by March 1972. Over a four-year period the bogie repair programme on class 86 cost some £150,000, with little guarantee that it would not recur.

Tests to establish an estimate of the fatigue life of the bogie frame were undertaken on locomotive E3119 as soon as it left the works with repaired bogies. A fatigue life of only six years was predicted for a particular welded joint in the bogie side frame once operation on the much increased service mileage on Anglo-Scottish duties commenced. A new bogie frame design was necessary.

In late 1969, when increased operating speeds of up to 110mph were being proposed, studies were undertaken on how class 86 could be modified to permit such running. It was readily apparent that at 100mph problems with the 86 existed and the following aspects were studied:

A. Riding qualities as experienced by locomotive crews and by body-mounted equipment.

B. Environment of traction motor, with special attention to the dynamic accelera-tions transmitted to the commutators and brush gear.

C. Dynamic wheel/rail forces experienced over vertical rail irregularities at high speed, with special attention to track damage and locomotive wheel damage.

D. Assessment of the bogie frame modifica-tions and the increasing incidence of bogie frame fractures.

At this time BR was thinking of trials, with an AC locomotive hauling trains at up to 125mph on the line between Berkhamsted and Leighton Buzzard. The trials were to test overhead equipment and pantographs, with a view to development work for the future; to test the behaviour of locomotives, coaching stock and track; and also the drivers' ability to observe signals correctly at such speeds. From these tests future decisions on traction development were made. One factor examined was the best aerodynamic shape for the front of a locomotive, a factor greatly neglected in the BR AC locomotive fleet with the slab fronts and basic box-like outline, which certainly do not equal the efforts achieved with BR diesel locomotives. E3173 was fitted with a glass-fibre streamlined front for these tests.

The class 86 suffered from the use of the axle-hung traction motor with its high unsprung weights and high-speed operation. This severely punished the track, resulting in a spate of broken rails. This was largely attributed to class 86 running at around 100mph. Unfortunately, economic conditions did not permit replacements for the penalty the traction motors had placed on class 86.

The exact cause of rail damage and breakage was not known, and a programme was instigated to consider the factors which might cause the damage. Breakage occurred on sections of line permitting 100mph running and over, and when it was considered that on the East Coast main line the Deltic diesel-electric locomotives, with axle-hung traction motors, operated at similar speeds and above without detrimental effect to the track, their lower axle loading of only 17½ tons, and their Co-Co axle layout, was found to be an important factor. Class 86 on the other hand had a 20½-ton axle loading and only Bo-Bo layout. It was obvious that unless changes were made the troubles would be extended to the whole of the West Coast lines over which class 86 was to run.

As part of the tests, the BR Civil Engineer's department constructed a special dipped rail joint just north of Cheddington, with the object of measuring loads exerted on the track by various BR locomotives passing over it at speeds of up to 125mph. To compare the loads, an 86 with flexicoil secondary suspension, a standard 86, and an 85 with frame mounted motors, were tested on the line concerned. From these tests it became obvious that a different traction motor suspension was desirable. However, the existing motor of class 86 was not suitable for modification.

Attention was drawn to the Swedish rubber-cushioned wheel being used in a number of countries on locomotives with axle-hung traction motors, reducing track forces to a low level. The SAB wheel, designed and made by Svenska Aktiebolaget Bromsregulator of Malmo, Sweden, overcame the problem of the weight of axleboxes, wheel set, and half that of the traction motor resting unsprung on the rails.

In the SAB wheel, only the weight of the tyres and tyre disc rests unsprung on the rails. The axle, axleboxes, springs, and motor are suspended by the resilience of the SAB wheel, shocks and stresses are greatly reduced, while both the track and the locomotive is protected.

During September 1971 class 86 E3129 and E3173 were fitted with SAB wheels; subsequent tests on a dipped joint on the up fast line at Wrine Hill indicated a 50 percent drop in dynamic forces on track and sleepers at 100mph compared to the standard solid wheels of class 86. This was equivalent to a reduction in the unsprung mass to 1½ tons from 4½ tons. Tests undertaken by GEC Traction on traction motor environment showed that peak traction motor frame accelerations were reduced by 20-45 percent with SAB wheels. No benefit was, however, found in armature torque fluctuations at vertical rail irregularities, nor for the motor shaft or gear teeth. It was also found that the riding of E3173 with flexicoil secondary

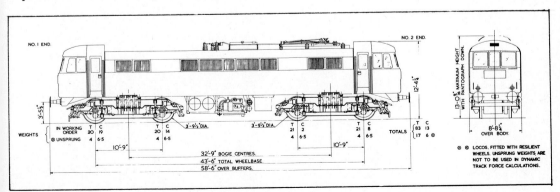

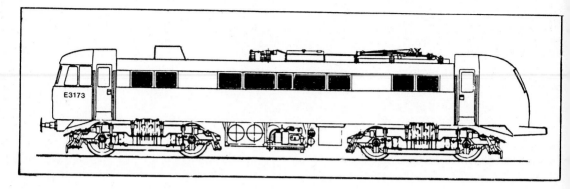

suspension was not altered to any extent by use of the SAB resilient wheel, provided a secondary yaw restraint damper was fitted; in all planes, vertical, lateral, and longitudinal, the riding of this locomotive was far superior to the standard 86.

Following initial success when the SAB wheel

CLASSES 86/1 AND 86/2 NAMES

In the summer of 1978 it was decided to include some class 86/1 and 86/2 locomotives in the list of those electric locomotives to be named. The list is as announced in early 1979.

No	Name	Naming Date	Place of Ceremony
86101	*Sir William A. Stanier FRS*	27/10/78	Liverpool
86204	*City of Carlisle*	7/12/78	Carlisle
86205	*City of Lancaster*		
86206	*City of Stoke on Trent*		
86207	*City of Lichfield*		
86208	*City of Chester*	7/3/79	Chester
86209	*City of Coventry*		
86210	*City of Edinburgh*	27/2/79	Edinburgh
86211	*City of Milton Keynes*		
86212	*Preston Guild*		
86213	*Lancashire Witch*		
86214	*Sanspareil*		
86215	*Comet*		
86216	*Meteor*		
86217	*Novelty*		
86218	*Planet*		
86219	*Phoenix*		
86220	*Goliath*		
86221	*Vesta*		
86222	*Fury*		
86223	*Hector*		
86224	*Caledonian*		
86225	*Hardwicke*		
86226	*Mail*		
86227	*Lady of the Lake*		
86240	*Bishop Eric Treacy*	3/4/79	Penrith
86241	*Glenfiddich*	28/3/79	Glasgow

86207 Originally to be *City of Chester*
86208 Originally to be *City of Lichfield*
86210 Originally to be *Hardwicke*, then *City of Preston*. (Preston is not a city)

86212 Originally to be *City of Edinburgh*
86215 Originally to be *Novelty*
86217 Originally to be *Comet*
86225 Originally to be *Lion*, then *Mentor*

was in large-scale use on BR, failures of the rubbers occurred at the bond between the rubbers and their backing plates. The plate nearest the tyre was always the one at fault and the cause traced to the locomotives being driven or hauled with dragging hand brakes or power brakes, the resulting overheating of the wheels causing the failure. By changing the composition of the rubber and modifying the bonding technique, improving the air flow between the backing plate and the tyre, and fitting warning buzzers to indicate to the driver that he was taking power with the locomotive brakes applied, this fault was overcome.

The intention to electrify the West Coast main line from Crewe to Glasgow included the motive power reappraisal which resulted in the refurbishing programmes for classes 83 and 84, as set out in Chapters 7 and 8, and included 34 new locomotives (class 87), later increased to 36, and the upgrading of class 86. It was decided to modify three VF-built class 86 at Crewe with the new bogie and frame-mounted traction motors intended for the new class 87, to gain running experience. These bogies had flexicoil suspension and in 1972 E3143/50/91 were so converted, and classified 86/1.

In addition, 49 class 86 were to be modified with new bogie frames and flexicoil suspension to achieve a performance capability on a par with the proposed class 87. These 49 locomotives were classified 86/2, leaving 48 with original bogies. Since then more locomotives have become class 86/2, leaving only 39 in their original form as class 86/0. From 1973/4 class 86 was fitted with air-operated, twin-ejector sanding gear.

In the autumn of 1970 E3173, geared for high-speed running, was used in tests to ascertain the part played by aero-dynamics in mechanical parts design. This utilitarian locomotive was again

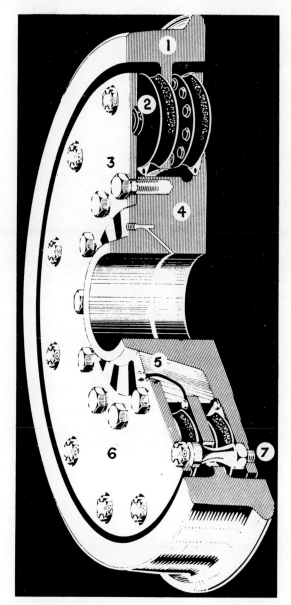

fitted with a glass-fibre false front end, roughly similar in shape to that then being proposed for the High Speed Train (HST), and a roof-top translucent dome to enable observation of the pantograph at speed.

Tests indicated that compared to a conventional class 86 E3173 was 25 percent better so far as pressure-wave effects were concerned, a fact of great importance to BR with a train-to-train side clearance of only 0.66m when passing at very high speeds, as would be the case with the HST in service, not to mention the effect on stations and people in close proximity to such trains. On Sundays in late 1970 the fast lines between Tring and Leighton Buzzard were used for various locomotives and rolling stock running at high speeds — E3173 both with and without its plastic nose, class 55 D9020 *Nimbus,* and a Clacton line EMU set. The station at Cheddington was used to test items of equipment and also artificial passengers to ascertain the effect of trains passing at very high speeds. In July 1971 further tests were undertaken which involved E3126 on a train from Hemel Hempstead passing E3173 with plastic nose on a train from Harrow in the confines of Watford tunnel at 110mph.

In May 1973 tests with E3173, with its traction motors regeared to a ratio of 61:26, were run at up to 125mph without over-speeding its motors, reports suggesting that in fact 128mph was attained at least once.

In June 1973 further high-speed running took place on the Beattock Summit-Ecclefechan section — with two 86/2 locomotives, one on the front and one on the rear of a four-coach set. With the leading locomotive working, 100mph was reached at Beattock, and with the rear locomotive assisting, 125mph between Murthat and Dinwoodie, and then with the rear locomotive cut out, the train reached 129mph near Nethercleugh. All this running was no doubt in connection with the HST and APT projects. One 86/2 was used for five weeks in 1977, to test the type of pantograph intended for the AC APT, 86254 being the locomotive concerned. It was towed by another locomotive, the trial pantograph not taking power.

Original deliveries of class 86 began from Vulcan Foundry in July 1965 and from Doncaster

Above: The SAB resilient wheel used in class 86/2 to improve the effect of the original bogie of class 86/0 in regard to high speed work, and its effect on the track due to the use of axle-hung traction motors. All class 86/2 have this wheel.

1 Tyre integral with middle wheel disc.
2 Pairs of rubber blocks compressed between outer, middle and inner (wheel centre) discs.
3 Outer disc securing bolt. 4 Inner wheel centre disc.
5 Electrical earthing connection between middle (tyre) disc and wheel hub, carrying the current from wheel centre to tyre.
6 Outer disc.
7 Distance bolt securing outer disc to middle (wheel centre) disc. *(SAB)*

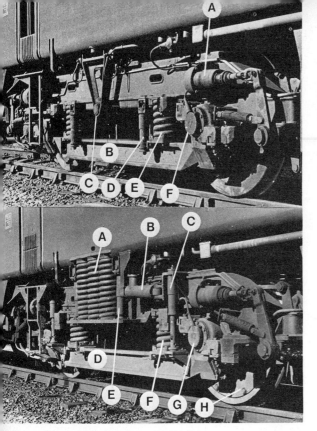

Above: Class 86/1 bogie. An advanced design high-speed bogie, with bogie-mounted traction motors. This bogie is the prototype for that used in class 87, and is unique in BR AC practice in having one-piece wheel and tyre.

A Sandbox lid.
B Secondary dampers controlling action of the secondary springs. Lateral dampers not shown.
C Secondary coil springs mounted between reinforced sections on locomotive body and platforms on the bogie frames.
D Yaw damper to control the turning of the bogie in relation to locomotive body on curved track.
E Primary damper mounted on the axlebox.
F Primary coil springs.
G Base of sand box with trap and primary ejector which forces compressed air through a coned nozzle. This creates a vacuum causing the sand to flow down the pipe to the rail.
H Sandpipe.
J Combined brake cylinder and slack adjuster.
K Roller bearing axlebox with mileometer and Alsthom links.   *(John Duncan)*

Above: Class 86/0 and 86/2 bogies.
Top: Class 86/0 bogies similar to classes 81 and 85 but with axle hung traction motors.

A Brake cylinder.
B Equalising beam.
C Body to bogie safety bracket which allows bogie to be lifted along with the locomotive body.
D Primary damper.
E Primary coil springs.
F Roller bearing axlebox with AEI speedometer generator, and Alsthom links.

Bottom: Class 86/2 bogie modified from 86/0 type.

A Flexicoil secondary springs.
B Yaw damper.
C Primary damper between bogie frame and equalising beam.
D Equalising beam.
E Secondary damper.
F Primary coil springs between bogie frame and equalising beam.
G Roller bearing axlebox and speedometer generator. Alsthom links control axlebox vertical movements.
H SAB resilient wheel. This reduces the unsprung mass from 4½ tons (class 86/0) to 1½ tons (class 86/2).   *(John Duncan)*

works in September 1965. The locomotives were allocated to AC lines, some in common with classes 81 and 85 being lent to Shields depot at Glasgow in 1974. All variants of the class are now based at Willesden depot. Class 86/0 is being progressively fitted with multiple-unit control and jumper cables, together with electronic wheelslip and over-speed control, for hauling freightliners. Their work is arranged so that the 86/1 and 86/2 units, together with class 87, are on the principal mainline passenger workings.

Tyre spalling and shelling, or breakage of the wheel tyre treads, occurred on classes 86 and 87. This was caused by the simultaneous use of rheostatic braking and the locomotive tread brakes, setting up rapid heating and cooling actions each time braking was applied. At one point discs of metal similar to 10p pieces were leaving the tyres, necessitating tyre turning at frequent intervals and cutting down tyre life. Tests with alternative grades of steel failed to improve the situation. It was found after investigation that the problem was not caused by the rheostatic brake, so modifications to the locomotive equipment were undertaken, which applied rheostatic braking at a different time from the tread brakes, the latter's use being avoided entirely at high speeds. A sixfold increase in mileage was achieved. Class 87 in addition suffered from short lengths of flats on tyres, because of the lower-placed tread brake rigging gripping and releasing the wheels for short periods

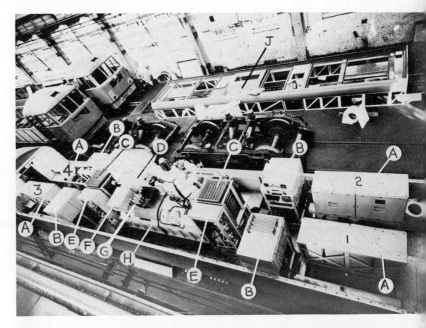

Right: Class 86/0 locomotives under construction at BR Doncaster works.

Key: **1-4** are power packs — one for each traction motor.

A Power pack housing rectifiers, smoothing choke and blower motor for one traction motor (No 4 is not complete).

B Power pack control and power contactors, switches, and relays.

C Rheostatic brake shutters which fit into roof.

D Oil immersed tap changer.

E Air and vacuum brake equipment cupboards.

F Tap changer motor and camshaft.

G Three high voltage diverter contactors.

H Main transformer.

J Roof and bodyside top structure awaiting fitting.   *(British Rail)*

Cab of 86/2 86222 approaching Carnforth with the 07.05 Glasgow-Euston 14 March 1978 through a very heavy rain shower.

Key: **1** Main air reservoir pressure gauge 118lb/sq in to 140lb/sq in.

2 Brake cylinder pressure gauge. One pointer for each bogie.

3 Vacuum gauge (not in use on this train due to air braked stock).

4 Automatic air brake pipe gauge reading 72.5lb/sq in indicating brakes are fully released.

5 Speedometer reading 90mph.

6 Traction motor 1 and 2 Ammeter reading 150A.

7 Traction motor 3 and 4 Ammeter reading 150A.

8 Notch indicator showing just below 25 percent tap from main transformer.

9 Three indicator lights: Top — line light indicating ABCB is closed and pantograph up.

10 Window wiper valve.

11 Horn valve handle.

12 Four push-button switches:
Top left-hand pantograph up and reset button;
Lower left-hand pantograph down button;
Top right-hand train heat on button;
Lower right-hand train heat off button.

13 AWS reset button.

14 Reversing lever in forward position.

15 Reversing handle interlock button.

16 Notching lever in 'run down' position. Power is being shut-off   *(John Duncan)*

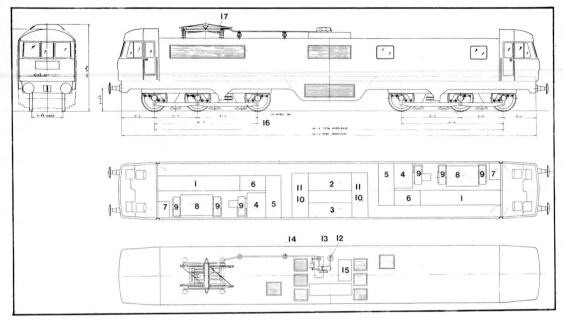

Although it is likely that BR will choose a Co-Co layout
for its next AC locomotive design, it has been done
before. Here is a 1965 proposal by AEI for an 8000hp
unit for mixed 750V DC and 25kV AC operation through
the Channel Tunnel.

Length over headstocks	65ft 0in
Total wheelbase	54ft 6in
Bogie wheelbase	16ft 0in
Height over roof	12ft 4¼in
Height over pantograph	13ft 9/16in (lowered)
Wheel diameter	3ft 9in

Key: **1** Control equipment
     2 Transformer
     3 Radiator

4 Choke
5 Rectifiers
6 Compressors
7 Exhausters
8 Motor generator sets
9 Blowers
10 Braking resistors
11 Starting resistors
12 Input bushing
13 Air blast circuit breaker
14 Surge diverter
15 Conservator
16 Third-rail current collector shoe (DC)
17 Pantograph (AC)   *(GEC Traction)*

and which caused the wheels to lock and slide.

As deliveries of class 86 proceeded, thinking in
the UK electrical industry was being focused on
the mooted channel tunnel between England and
France. This was to be a rail tunnel operated by
electric traction, as ventilation alone ruled out any
form of diesel or gas turbine propulsion. The
schemes, some involving costly new railways
between London and the south coast, electrified
on the 25kV AC system, were considered.
However, at least one British manufacturer
thought otherwise. This was AEI, the Traction
Division at Trafford Park at one point in its
deliberations proposing a system involving dual-
system AC and DC. This made use of existing SR
third-rail DC, while at the same time could use AC
at 25kV through the tunnel itself.

To this end a Co-Co electric locomotive was
proposed which had DC third-rail collector shoes
on the bogies, and a pantograph for the AC

overhead wire system. This machine was
proposed in early 1966 and was of 8000hp. As can
be seen from the diagram, this locomotive would
have been very similar in appearance to the
existing BR AC locomotive fleet.

Political impasse, and lack of courage so far as
the governments of the day were concerned, in due
course stopped further progress on this important
link with Europe, which if completed would have
heralded the second railway age considerably
earlier than the era which may yet result when the
oil runs out! Fortunately, the channel tunnel
scheme as a rail only link to Europe has again been
brought out of limbo as a simpler scheme with a
single line tunnel connected to the existing rail
network on each side. Let us hope that the idea will
not again be smothered by long debate and
indecision and that freight and passenger trains
will be operating through a channel tunnel within
the next ten to twelve years.

CLASS 86 (AL6) NUMBERING AND CONSTRUCTION DETAILS

Main contractor: English Electric Co Ltd/AEI
Builders of locomotives: BR Doncaster (E3101-E3140)
  Vulcan Foundry Ltd (E3141-E3200)

Details of Numbering and Renumbering			Maker's Number	Maker's No Order No	Date Traffic
E3101	86252			E020	P9/65
E3102	86009			E020	P9/65
E3103	86004			E020	P9/65
E3104	86010			E020	P10/65
E3105	86030			E020	P7/65
E3106	86214			E020	P7/65
E3107	86248			E020	P10/65
E3108	86038			E020	P7/65
E3109	86016			E020	P7/65
E3110	86027			E020	P7/65
E3111	86024			E024	P7/65
E3112	86006			E024	P9/65
E3113	86232			E024	P9/65
E3114	86020			E024	P10/65
E3115	86003			E024	P10/65
E3116	86238			E024	P10/65
E3117	86227			E024	P10/65
E3118	86041	86261		E024	P10/65
E3119	86229			E024	P10/65
E3120	86019			E024	P10/65
E3121	86241			E025	P10/65
E3122	86012			E025	P10/65
E3123	86015			E025	P11/65
E3124	86035			E025	P11/65
E3125	86209			E025	P12/65
E3126	86231			E025	P11/65
E3127	86240			E025	P11/65
E3128	86013			E025	P12/65
E3129	86205			E025	P12/65
E3130	86037			E025	P13/65
E3131	86222			E026	P13/65
E3132	86221			E026	P13/65
E3133	86236			E026	P13/65
E3134	86224			E026	P13/65
E3135	86040	86256		E026	P1/66
E3136	86044	86253		E026	P13/65
E3137	86045	86259		E026	P1/66
E3138	86242			E026	P1/66
E3139	86043	86257		E026	P1/66
E3140	86046	86258		E026	P3/66
E3141	86208		3722	E382	P2/66
E3142	86047	86254	3723	E383	P2/66
E3143	86203	86103	3724	E384	P3/66
E3144	86048	86260	3725	E385	P3/66
E3145	86014		3726	E386	P3/66
E3146	86017		3727	E387	P4/66
E3147	86211		3728	E388	P4/66
E3148	86032		3729	E389	P4/66
E3149	86246		3730	E390	P4/66
E3150	86202	86102	3731	E391	P4/66
E3151	86212		3732	E392	P4/66
E3152	86023		3733	E393	P5/66
E3153	86039		3734	E394	P5/66
E3154	86042	86255	3735	E395	P5/66
E3155	86234		3736	E396	P6/66
E3156	86220		3737	E397	P7/66
E3157	86021		3738	E398	P7/66
E3158	86223		3739	E399	P7/66
E3159	86028		3740	E400	P7/66
E3160	86036		3741	E401	P11/66
E3161	86249		3453	E299	P10/65
E3162	86226		3454	E300	P9/65
E3163	86018		3455	E301	P9/65
E3164	86225		3456	E302	P9/65
E3165	86215		3457	E303	P9/65
E3166	86216		3458	E304	P10/65
E3167	86228		3459	E305	P9/65
E3168	86230		3460	E306	P7/65
E3169	86239		3461	E307	P7/65
E3170	86002		3462	E308	P7/65
E3171	86011		3463	E309	P10/65
E3172	86233		3464	E310	P7/65
E3173	86204		3465	E311	P9/65
E3174	86022		3466	E312	P9/65
E3175	86218		3467	E313	P10/65
E3176	86007		3468	E314	P9/65
E3177	86217		3469	E315	P9/65
E3178	86244		3470	E316	P9/65
E3179	86207		3471	E317	P10/65
E3180	86008		3472	E318	P10/65
E3181	86243		3473	E319	P11/65
E3182	86245		3474	E320	P10/65
E3183	86251		3475	E321	P11/65
E3184	86206		3476	E322	P10/65
E3185	86005		3477	E323	P10/65
E3186	86025		3478	E324	P11/65
E3187	86034		3479	E325	P11/65
E3188	86031		3480	E326	P11/65
E3189	86250		3481	E327	P12/65
E3190	86210		3482	E328	P11/65
E3191	86201	86101	3483	E329	P12/65
E3192	86247		3484	E330	P12/65
E3193	86213		3485	E331	P12/65
E3194	86235		3486	E332	P13/65
E3195	86026		3487	E333	P13/65
E3196	86219		3488	E334	P13/65
E3197	86237		3489	E335	P13/65
E3198	86033		3490	E336	P1/66
E3199	86001		3491	E337	P2/66
E3200	86029		3492	E338	P2/66

NOTES

EE/VF	locomotives built under EE order No CCS 1348, VF order 6420 (E3161-79)
6421	(E3180-3200), and EE order No CCR 1348, VF order 6673 (E3141-60)
86/0	Allocated numbers 86001-48 with original bogies.
86/2	Allocated numbers 86501-52 originally, but became 86204-52, bogies fitted with flexicoil suspension.
E3191/50/43	
	Allocated numbers 86501-3 but became 86201-3, and then 86101-3. These locomotives have class 87 bogies, and are classified 86/1.
86040-8	Subsequently fitted with Flexicoil suspension as 86/2 and numbered 86253-61.

CHAPTER 11

CLASS 87, THE *ROYAL SCOT* CLASS

The latest of the BR AC locomotive family which owes its origin to the initial 100 locomotives is class 87. This type may well be the last of this line of development. At the time of writing, class 87 represents the most advanced AC locomotive on British Rail, being introduced in 1973, built at Crewe works with electrical equipment manufactured and supplied by GEC Traction Ltd (GECT). They provide the motive power for the principal West Coast Main Line passenger services, being geared for 110mph maxima, and are supplemented by the class 86/2.

With a continuous rating of 5000hp (3750kW) in weak field, the locomotives were designed with an eye to the gradients on the Crewe-Glasgow section on which they were intended to haul 450-ton passenger trains, and 750-ton freights single-handed.

Although class 87 is generally similar to class 86, the main differences externally are bogies with flexicoil secondary suspension, windscreen formed of two panels instead of three, elimination of cab-front four-digit train identification panels, fitting of sanding gear (later fitted to class 86), multiple-unit operation equipment, and train air braking only. More important is the return to a frame-mounted traction motor.

The mechanical portion comprises an underframe fabricated by welding and integrally constructed from steel plate and folded sections. This takes the form of a single longitudinal box section assembly made up of 8mm thick longitudinal and lateral webs enclosed by 11mm thick top and bottom plates.

Like classes 85 and 86, the upper body sides can be lifted off as a complete unit to permit access at times of major overhaul. The roof has translucent panels. Bogies without inter-connecting linkages are fitted. Unsprung weight has been reduced to only 2.6 tons per axle; solid-rolled monobloc wheels are fitted. Following the practice used in classes 81 and 85, the Timken roller-bearing axleboxes are controlled by radius arm links held by Metalastik rubber bushed pins. Primary suspension is by vertical coil springs placed fore and aft of the axleboxes, one above, one below the box centreline.

Triple flexicoil groups give secondary suspension. They are 640mm high under compression. The springs are pitched at 280mm centres and carry 11 tons per set, or one quarter of the body weight of 44 tons. These give torsional stiffness when the bogies are negotiating curves, and control locomotive riding. Damping throughout the bogie is by Koni dampers, two working in conjunction with the flexicoil units, and one each side linking the kingpin with the bogie side frames. One is also fitted on the top of each of the axleboxes and fixed to the bogie frame. The bogies are arranged with the nominal centre line of the kingpin connection 60mm below the axlebox centre line. The traction and braking forces are transmitted through the kingpin.

The side frames pass over the axleboxes and drop down only at the ends to connect up with the headstocks. The centre transom drops down and receives the kingpin connection which is formed of two laminated-rubber traction pads, one placed fore, one aft, between which a steel-bronzed, bushed casting is sandwiched under a compression loading of some ten tons. Bogie rotation is through the two rubber traction pads, the kingpin casting being unable to rotate. To assist assembly, the casting is assembled into the bogie.

Arrangement of the class 87 traction motor and drive; also fitted to class 86/1. *(GEC Traction)*

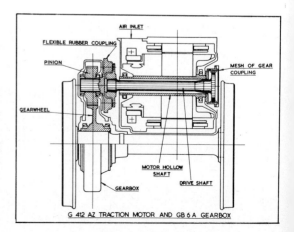

G 412 AZ TRACTION MOTOR AND GB 6 A GEARBOX

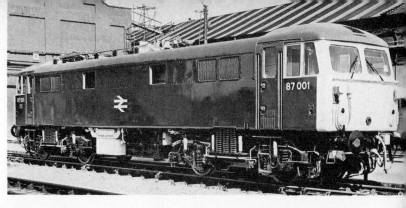

The first class 87, 87001, standing in the yard of BREL, Crewe when new in 1973. This class had the Flexicoil bogie from the start, and is the only BR AC locomotive class with two rather than three cab front windows. Note too elimination of the cab-front train description box, and the provision of multiple unit control.

(GEC Traction)

Class 87 is fitted with GECT type G412 AZ, four-pole, series wound, DC traction motors, with interpoles and compensating windings. Their one-hour rating is 950kW, 1134V, 885A, giving 1270hp at 1360rpm. Unique in BR practice, the motor has three-point suspension in the bogie though flexible rubber mountings. The spur gears have single reduction drive, and are enclosed in a gearbox supported on the axle by tapered roller bearings and from the bogies by a rubber-bushed torque reaction link. The gearwheel is directly mounted on the axle, while the pinion is mounted on a shaft running in tapered roller bearings in the gearbox.

To overcome the relative motion between motor and gearbox, the drive torque is transmitted by a long driving shaft passing through the hollow shaft of the motor. The driving shaft has angular flexibility and freedom for axial movement by being coupled to the motor through a gear type coupling which is fitted under the back end of the armature windings. Its other end is coupled by means of a flexible rubber-bushed coupling to the pinion shaft. The gear ratio is 73:32. The motors have a permanent field divert of 16 percent, with an operational weak field current diversion of an additional 23 percent in a single stage. This gives maximum utilisation of locomotive capacity over its speed range.

Rheostatic braking is identical to Class 86, and is controlled by separately exciting the motor fields, whilst the armatures are connected to a bank of resistors to dissipate power. The control is similar to that of class 86, but the class 87 was fitted from new for multiple-unit operation with electronic wheelslip and over-speed protection.

Current collection is by one cross-arm GECT pantograph, roof mounted to the rear of No 1 cab. It has two copper-impregnated carbon rubbing strips designed for a contact thrust of 20lb. Low-friction joints with PTFE-lined sleeve bearings are fitted.

The main transformer is similar to that used in class 86, but adapted to increase its rating by 20 percent. The electric train heating winding load is also increased to take account of train air-conditioning requirements. The transformer consists of an auto-transformer tapped in 38 positions by an HT tap changer responding to the driver's master controller. The transformer is lighter in weight than that of class 86 by redesign and use of less oil. The windings are totally immersed in oil, which is pump-circulated for cooling. Gas accumulation warning is given by a Buchholz relay. The HT tap changer is similar to that in classes 82 and 86 but with modification to improve reliability. The power circuits comprise four identical power-pack groupings. Each has a transformer secondary winding bridge-connected silicon rectifier assembly, smoothing inductor and traction motor. The driver can isolate any one of these groups in the event of a fault, and operate the locomotive on reduced power.

Each of the four rectifier units supplies one traction motor and is cooled by the associated traction motor blower. Each locomotive has four separate bridge rectifiers, one per motor, and the rectifier cubicles are improved in rating and for maintenance compared with class 86, ie class 87 rectifiers only have 16 cells per cubicle, but the 86 has 96 cells. An auxiliary rectifier feeds the DC auxiliary machines.

Class 87 is fitted only for working air-braked trains, whereas classes 81-86 now have both vacuum and air-braking. Classes 85-87 also have rheostatic braking, although not yet fully operative on the majority of class 85s.

On 4 February 1976, 87003 working the 15.50 Manchester-Euston experienced a severe traction motor failure near Stoke-on-Trent. Upon inspection No 3 traction motor gearbox was found to have collapsed with overheated gearbox-pinion bearings. The cause was the gearbox housing working loose with the consequent loss of lubricating oil, and failure of the bearings. Both pinion and gearwheel were badly damaged by parts of the bearings reaching the gearwheel and lodging in its teeth. The outcome was that more

Above: 87012, *Coeur de Lion,* heads an up Glasgow-Euston express through Wreay on 21 July 1978.

(Brian Webb)

Below: Diagram of class 87   *(British Rail)*

maintenance attention was needed to the housing bolts, class 86/1 and 87 with identical motors being involved. Traction motor nose suspension bolt breakages arising from stretching of the bolts gave rise to loose traction motors, which in some instances were moving about in the locomotive bogie and rubbing on the wheels. New bolts of improved type were fitted.

Class 87 was fitted with hollow axles to reduce the unsprung mass. Unfortunately, BR ultrasonic axle-testing requirements meant that the frozen-in axle end-plugs fitted to provide a turning centre had to be taken out to allow access to the interior of the axles. The plugs were so difficult to remove that a modified plug was designed with a smaller interference fit and a tapped flange to enable the plug to be jacked out.

The incidence of axle-bearing failure started after this point, and it was found that the new plug was allowing a slight collapse of the hollow-axle ends. The screws retaining the bearing end-cap began to break, allowing half the tapered roller bearing to move outwards. The modification involved the use of longer retaining bolts as used before the fitting of the new end plugs, giving the bolts more stretch and lifting them out of the fatigue load range. Subsequently, solid axles have been progressively fitted to the class.

Riding qualities of the class 87 bogies proved disappointing. Tests showed this was partly due to inadequate lateral clearance between the locomotive body bump stops and the bogie frame, which indicated that the lateral damping was inadequate. This problem was overcome by each locomotive visiting Crewe locomotive works to have the clearances enlarged and permit the

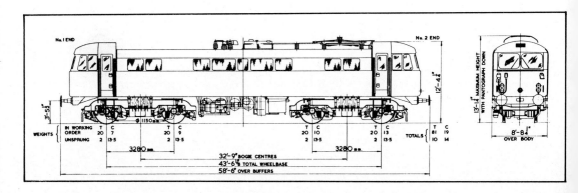

damping arrangement to be corrected.

Another bogie problem found in 1978 was the fracturing of the bogie-yaw damper bracket welds on the body. Rewelding is in process; a revised specification will hopefully prevent future fractures.

Class 87 has brake cylinders similar to class 40 diesel-electric locomotives. In class 87, the brake cylinders are mounted directly on the bogie adjacent to the wheel, one cylinder per brake block. In the early operation of class 87 inadequate seals in the cylinders caused brake block dust to enter, with the result that seizing occurred in both brake 'on' and 'off' positions. Modified seals have greatly improved the situation.

Classes 86/1 and 87 have hydraulically-operated handbrakes, the driver simply turning a switch which pumps oil under pressure to a cylinder and applies the four inner brake blocks on each bogie. Again, oil leakages at seals caused problems at first until improved seals were fitted.

High-speed wheelslip on gradients because of the high tractive effort of class 87 and the fact that it is of Bo-Bo, rather than Co-Co, layout is a problem. Bo-Bo locomotives suffer from weight transfer during acceleration, with the result that adhesion on the leading axle of each bogie is reduced. Each traction motor of an 87 has an output of 1250hp, equivalent to a class 25 diesel-electric locomotive on each 87 axle!

One step towards combating wheelslip is the experimental work on locomotives 87018 and 87025 fitted with compressed air operated high-velocity sanding gear. This system overcomes sanding deficiencies in high winds so that sand is actually blown under the locomotive wheels, rather than being blown away by the wind. Aerodynamic problems in getting the sand through the cushion of air around the wheel caused difficulties.

Locomotives 87025/31/2/3/5 were fitted in 1975 with GECT vacuum circuit breakers instead of air-blast circuit breakers. Some trouble with the VCB has given rise to problems, including welding of the contacts by excessive arcing, due to air leaking into the vacuum chambers. The main rectifier trays of glass-fibre developed hairline cracks, so allowing carbon dust into the cracks, lowering insulation, and causing short circuits. GECT is modifying all the trays at Reddish depot, the depot for the 1500V DC locomotives on BR! The class 87s were the first electric locomotives

to be built at Crewe, body shells for 87001-7 being under construction towards the end of 1972. The first locomotive, 87001, was equipped by mid-January 1973 and others were in progress up to 87010. It was in March that 87001 was painted and not until June when it was observed at work, officially going into stock in June 1973.

As the 87s appeared they were put on to general West Coast diagrams as Euston-Preston workings had been instigated, and by July four or five locomotives were allocated to Willesden. The Royal Scot trains were 87-hauled from 22 April 1974, and reduced the Euston-Glasgow time from six to five hours.

The final locomotive, intended as 87036, was to be thyristor controlled and was well advanced in November 1974, but February 1975 saw the number 87101 being used for the locomotive. It was in restricted service by March 1975 and was allocated to the research department for testing, being limited in its sphere of work because of the potential interference with telecommunications by its thyristor equipment. It was allocated to Willesden in January 1977, but remained a development locomotive, largely under the aegis of GECT; nevertheless, it was on revenue-earning duties.

Since the introduction of the computer Total Operating and Processing System (TOPS) on BR, the maintenance of the whole of the AC locomotive fleet has been computer-based. By this system a locomotive is logged on its duty hours and as it reaches its various examination periods, it cannot be re-rostered until it has gone through the examination, the computer refusing to accept the locomotive concerned. The smaller A and B examinations are carried out as required at any AC locomotive depot, the A examination after 120 hours' duty, B examination after 360 hours, while C examinations after 720 hours' duty are carried out at home depots only. Other examinations are D, E, F at 1440, 2880, and 5760 hours respectively.

The 150 years' celebrations of the Stockton & Darlington Railway in 1975 prompted the Stephenson Locomotive Society to offer BR nameplates to commemorate George Stephenson, but simply lettered *Stephenson*, to be fixed on a modern locomotive. Class 87 87001 was chosen and the naming ceremony was held at Euston station on 14 January 1976, when the president of the SLS, A.J. Boston, unveiled the plates on the locomotives. The plates were of stainless steel with engraved lettering, and in addition to the name also carried 'Named by the Stephenson Locomotive Society 1975'. In 1977 it was decided to name the whole of class 87 under the general title of 'Royal Scot' class, following in the footsteps (or should it be wheel treads) of their famous steam predecessors, although with names drawn from many locomotive classes of the past. To this end 87001 was renamed after consultation with the SLS, the *Stephenson* plates being moved to the thyristor locomotive 87101 which was officially named by A.J. Boston on 12 October 1977 at Manchester Piccadilly station. 87001 became *Royal Scot* on 14 July 1977. Naming of selected locomotives at special ceremonies was carried out, but the remainder had nameplates fitted without ceremony at Willesden depot at suitable opportunities.

The cost of the nameplates and their fixing received some hostile press comment, but the nameplates require some ingenuity in fixing, especially on the equipment side of the locomotive body, where one of the two-man team had to crawl along the air ducting tunnel to gain access behind the nameplate position. BR is to be congratulated on its more flexible attitude to naming of its locomotives. Long may it continue.

CLASS 87 NUMBERING AND CONSTRUCTION DETAILS

| Traction equipment contractor: | GEC Traction |
| Builder of locomotives: | BREL Crewe |

Numbering	Date into traffic	
87001	June	1973
87002	June	1973
87003	July	1973
87004	July	1973
87005	August	1973
87006	November	1973
87007	October	1973
87008	November	1973
87009	November	1973
87010	December	1973
87011	January	1974
87012	January	1974
87013	February	1974
87014	January	1974
87015	February	1974
87016	March	1974
87017	March	1974
87018	May	1974
87019	March	1974
87020	March	1974
87021	April	1974
87022	April	1974
87023	April	1974
87024	April	1974
87025	April	1974
87026	May	1974
87027	May	1974
87028	May	1974
87029	June	1974
87030	June	1974
87031	July	1974
87032	July	1974
87033	August	1974
87034	September	1974
87035	October	1974
87101	January	1977

NOTE

87101 allocated No 87036 but did not enter traffic with it. Delivered for research purposes in March 1975 but not officially into traffic until January 1977.

CLASSES 87 and 87/1 NAMES AND NAMING DATES

No	Name	Naming Date	Place of Ceremony
87001	Royal Scot	14/7/77	Manchester
87002	Royal Sovereign	4/7/78	
87003	Patriot	13/6/78	
87004	Britannia	3/4/78	Crewe
87005	City of London	22/11/77	
87006	City of Glasgow	8/12/77	
87007	City of Manchester	1/11/77	
87008	City of Liverpool	29/11/77	
87009	City of Birmingham	29/11/77	
87010	King Arthur	6/6/78	
87011	The Black Prince	15/5/78	
87012	Coeur de Lion	25/5/78	
87013	John o' Gaunt	14/3/78	Lancaster
87014	Knight of the Thistle	16/5/78	
87015	Howard of Effingham	12/5/78	
87016	Sir Francis Drake	28/4/78	
87017	Iron Duke	30/5/78	
87018	Lord Nelson	9/3/78	Liverpool
87019	Sir Winston Churchill	3/5/78	
87020	North Briton	19/5/78	
87021	Robert the Bruce	12/6/78	
87022	Cock o' the North	30/6/78	
87023	Highland Chieftain	3/7/78	
87024	Lord of the Isles	24/5/78	
87025	Borderer	6/6/78	
87026	Redgauntlet	19/5/78	
87027	Wolf of Badenoch	18/5/78	
87028	Lord President	9/5/78	
87029	Earl Marischal	26/6/78	
87030	Black Douglas	10/7/78	
87031	Hal o' the Wynd	8/6/78	
87032	Kenilworth	9/5/78	
87033	Thane of Fife	30/5/78	
87034	William Shakespeare	16/5/78	Birmingham International
87035	Robert Burns	13/4/78	Glasgow
87101	Stephenson	12/10/77	Manchester

NOTES 1. 87001 first named *Stephenson* at Euston 14 January 1976.

2. Remainder of class were named at Willesden depot without ceremony.

CHAPTER 12

BR EXPERIMENTAL LOCOMOTIVES AND EXPORTED AC LOCOMOTIVES

Apart from the low-power AC locomotives supplied to Norway in 1908, the first major involvement for British industry in AC locomotives was with the Hungarian State Railway main line electrification of the Budapest-Hegyeshalom section in the 1931-4 period. This 120-mile scheme involved overhead wire 16000V single-phase power tapped from a three-phase transmission line of industrial frequency at 50 cycles. This was a great step forward and the world's first single-phase industrial frequency electrification requiring locomotives.

Metropolitan Vickers, in addition to supplying static equipment for this scheme, became sub-contractors to Ganz & Co of Budapest for the supply of pantographs, control equipment and 30 MV-designed 2500hp AC main traction motors for 26 locomotives, including four spare motors. The locomotive mechanical parts were built at the Royal Hungarian state engineering works. Two types of locomotive each of 90 tons weight resulted, a 1-D-1 passenger locomotive and a six-axle all-powered freight locomotive. The design of the locomotives was on the Kando system

PROGRESSIVE DEVELOPMENTS IN POST-WAR BRITISH MAINLINE AC LOCOMOTIVE DESIGN

BR AL3 CLASS 83	Stepped tap changer Mercury-arc rectifier Bo-Bo 25kV
BR AL3 E3100	Transductor stepless tap changer (non-electronic) Silicon rectifier Bo-Bo 25kV
PAKISTAN WESTERN RAILWAY	Tap changer electronically controlled Silicon rectifier Thyristor Bo-Bo 25kV
BR 87/1 87101	No tap changer Thyristors and silicon rectifiers Bo-Bo 25kV
TAIWAN RAILWAYS	AS 87101 Bo-Bo 25kV 70T 18T per axle
SOUTH AFRICAN RAILWAYS 9E CLASS (ISCOR)	AS 87101 168T 28T per axle Co-Co 50kV
BRAZIL	Co-Co 25kV 180T 30T per axle

involving a single frame-mounted traction motor of AC type. This massive motor drove to the wheels via a form of jackshaft drive designed by Kalman Kando, incorporating a triangular driving frame, all wheels being rod-coupled.

So far as British AC locomotive work was concerned, the matter rested, until the decision by BR to go for main line AC electrification gave British industry its post-war introduction to modern AC locomotive work. The majority of the work undertaken at the design and development stage of BR classes 81-85 was very important. Nonetheless, it must be said that a fairly conservative approach was generally adopted.

It was to be the English Electric desire to try for something more advanced in one of the batch of AC locomotives it was then supplying to BR (class 83) which set the ball rolling. From this experimental locomotive, work progressed into the export field, to BR in a logical sequence, and again into exports.

The idea of fitting semi-conductor rectifiers, rather than mercury-arc rectifiers, to the whole of Class 83 had appealed to EE for some time, and in mid-1959 an idea to fit two locomotives, was discussed with the BTC. S.B. Warder, BR Chief Electrical Engineer, approved the scheme, provided that the locomotives concerned also received rheostatic braking equipment.

Rheostatic braking could not be incorporated as work was too advanced on the majority of the locomotives in the order. EE sought permission to carry out a simple substitution of silicon for mercury-arc rectifier on one locomotive, but this was not granted. A grander scheme concerning silicon rectifier/transductor equipment for the fifteenth locomotive in the batch was evolved. In order to demonstrate the proposal a test rig was set up at the EE works in Bradford and a party from the BTC saw the silicon/transductor equipment demonstrated in October 1960. A modified control scheme and rheostatic braking was proposed by EE and in due course given approval.

Finance for the scheme was the subject of long discussion, and in the end it was EE which stood most of the cost of the 'special locomotive', which was to provide much useful data for EE and BR.

The fifteenth locomotive was originally intended to be a type B locomotive geared for a maximum of 80mph, one of three to be numbered E3303-5. Eventually, it was decided that the first eleven locomotives would be type A, along with the fifteenth, this making the twelfth to fourteenth locomotives type B units. In the end only the thirteenth and fourteenth were built as type B locomotives because the final locomotive intended as E3305 was to be the special locomotive which was numbered E3100 and geared as a type A locomotive for 100mph running.

The transductors and smoothing chokes were located in the standard Class 83 reactor tank fitted on the first 14 locomotives, this being mounted under the locomotives between the bogies. The total weight of the tank and equipment was 3.95 tons.

It took some time to complete E3100 at Vulcan Foundry due to slower delivery of its special components but it was ready for testing there by late January 1962. To improve the riding of the locomotive, from experience gained with class 83 at higher speed, it was decided to lubricate the top bearing surfaces of the bogie sidebearers on E3100, before handing over to BR. Equipment tests were undertaken, together with brake and noise tests over a two-week period. E3100 was handed over to BR following tests and inspection, and delivered to Crewe works for weighing on 13 April 1962, with the following result:

	E3100			Standard Class 83		
Weight of locomotive including lead ballast weights	76T	7C	0Q	74T	12C	1Q
Total weight of lead ballast for balancing purposes	2T	1C	2Q	1T	13C	2Q
Weight of locomotive with all ballast removed	74T	5C	2Q	72T	18C	3Q

Later 6cwt of ballast weights were removed from E3100.

Externally E3100 differed little from its sister class 83s, apart from having one window on its 'A' side replaced by louvres, and a smaller roof-top circular grille at No 1 end over the silicon rectifier cooling unit, the standard 83 having a larger grille over the radiator cooling fan. E3100 also had prominent shutters on the roof at No 2 end over the rheostatic brake resistor duct. The louvre was fitted to improve air flow for cooling the rheostatic brake system; subsequently, both sides

of E3100 had louvres, three on the 'A' side and four on the 'B' side.

In its original form, E3100 had transductor assisted low-voltage tape changing arranged with notched current control which permitted standardised driving technique with the rest of class 83. Although test running was soon under way, E3100 was not taken into operating stock until July 1962. The transductors were in the secondary AC circuit between the conventional tap changer on the secondary transformer coil and rectifiers. With conventional tap changers, each time the driver notches up, the next tap is taken through the tap changer via the rectifiers to the traction motors, the voltage rising in steps, eg zero volts, 75 volts, 100 volts, 125 volts and so on. This progression gives large sudden increases in the turning force of the traction motors and is liable to cause wheelslip; to avoid this the driver is likely to notch up at a slower rate. This process does not make full use of the traction motor and tractive effort available. If a device is incorporated which converts the step by step process of increasing voltage into a smooth stepless increase, the chance of wheelslip is much reduced. E3100 had this form of control by using transductors, which might be compared to a sponge in its action. It is in fact a form of magnetic winding which when saturated produces high resistance in the circuit, and when unsaturated low resistance. This absorbs the sudden increase in voltage from the tap changer, so producing a smooth rise in voltage to the rectifiers and traction motors — stepless tap changing.

On E3100 control of the demanded tractive effort was automatic, the locomotive being able to haul heavier loads at greater acceleration than the standard 83 locomotive. While testing was in progress, the idea of sending E3100 to Europe for testing by ORE (L'Office de Recherches et D'Essais/The Office for Research and Experiments) was discussed by BR and EE. The ORE tests timed for May 1963 would enable a direct comparison, under identical conditions, of E3100 with French, German, and Swiss electric locomotives. During September 1962 it was decided to do additional work on E3100 providing that EE could have the locomotive ready for service by the end of February 1963 to permit trials in the UK before shipment.

This scheme no doubt appealed to the UK railway industry, for it provided a chance to regain some of the prestige which it was thought might have been lost due to severe problems with EMU

E3100 on test with dynamometer car, mobile test units
and test train incorporating three class 85 locomotives
to provide rheostatic brake power for adhesion tests,
between Crewe and Stafford in May 1963.

(GEC Traction)

E3100. CALIBRATION OF WEIGHT TRANSFER AIR
PRESSURE GAUGE TO EACH TRACTION
MOTOR AMMETER READING

Traction current, amps	700	800	1000	1200	1400
Air pressure lb/sq in	40	50	68	87	103

trains on BR AC lines, being made public in
reports published by the Railway Inspectorate
and the press. E3100 was to be modified to
incorporate notchless control. The mode of
control had constant current control of the
traction motors during acceleration and braking,
the reference current being determined by the
setting of the master controller. The first stage of
wheelslip was indicated by a warning light on the
driving desk; the second stage automatically
ensured that the traction motor current was
reduced until slip was arrested. Operation was
made much easier by this technique and full use of
the adhesion available made possible. Except in
weak field, a smooth tractive effort was assured.
With the traction motors connected in parallel and
the transductor control, together with a steep
tractive effort/speed characteristic, E3100 had all
the features requisite to give good adhesion
performance.

It was arranged that E3100 would return to EE
at VF, Newton-le-Willows, on 2 November 1962.
In order that an 80mph speed characteristic could
be provided, rather than regear the locomotive it
was decided to transfer to it both bogies from the
only remaining type B class 83 locomotive, E3304.
E3304 was sent to VF and upon receipt of E3100's
bogies became a type A locomotive. E3304 was
renumbered E3099 in December 1962.

A further modification carried out at the request
of EE was the fitting of weight-transfer
compensation equipment. Weight transfer at
acceleration/deceleration was compensated by air
cylinders operating on the locomotive bogie
headstocks.

The ammeter readings for all BR AC
locomotives are green, yellow and red. These
indicate normal current, short time rating, and
overload zone respectively. On E3100 for readings
of 707 amps and 1370 amps the equivalent air
pressure readings on the weight transfer pressure
gauge were 40lb/sq in and 100lb/sq in. These gave
a mechanical efficiency of 95 percent acting on the
inner bogie headstocks. Some difficulty in
housing additional equipment in an already full
locomotive body resulted in removal of the toilet
compartment on E3100 — obviously not required
for the ORE tests.

At one point consideration was given to fitting
EE type 544 traction motors to eliminate weak
field operation and give a smooth tractive effort
control under all operating conditions. This plan
was not carried out.

In May 1963 tests with E3100 between Stafford
and Crewe took place, the train being composed of
a dynamometer car and two mobile testing units.
Three class 85 locomotives with rheostatic
braking were added to the train. Control of the
train was from the dynamometer car which was
capable of absorbing a drawbar pull of up to
75000lb.

For three weeks tests were made at constant
speeds and with tractive effort raised through
smooth control to the point of wheelslip. In
favourable rail conditions this involved working at
tractive efforts of up to three times the continuous
rating of the equipment. The equipment was
found stable during early stages of wheelslip and

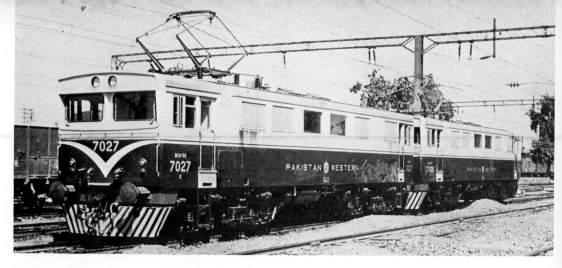

by increasing the currents on the non-slipping motors to give a higher drawbar pull, the slipping motor still contributed an appreciable tractive effort. The stability was the result of having traction motors in parallel and the very steep characteristic which is possible with the smooth control system, further coupled with good riding bogies with inherent low weight transfer properties and weight transfer compensation.

It was not possible to compare directly the performance of E3100 with a conventional AC locomotive under similar operating conditions. Tests were also incomplete because no locomotive with conventional notching and able to work at the high current values necessary to cause wheelslip under favourable conditions was available.

Both BR and EE reports stated that E3100 demonstrated excellent performance over a wide range of working conditions. Mr S. B. Warder said, 'It is evident that this design performs as well as, or even better than, designs incorporating single-motor bogies, without the mechanical complications of the latter, while preserving the simplicity and easy maintenance associated with individual axle drive.'

The ORE tests were postponed until October 1963, plans being to ship the locomotive, dynamometer car and mobile testing units to Europe following completion of BR road tests and tests of the locomotive's transmission efficiency at the BR locomotive testing station, Rugby. Unfortunately, the ORE tests were cancelled, the locomotive and its testing units not going to Europe.

BR intended at one time to test another type B locomotive for comparison at the 80mph limit. It was thought that E3301 from AEI (BTH) was the locomotive considered. However, as things turned out it was built as a type A locomotive, so no tests were possible.

As stated in Chapter 7, E3100 was converted to a standard class 83, as it was an 'odd man out', not through any lack of success. The transductor system was by that time being outmoded by the thyristor, so it had outlived its usefulness in that form anyway.

The experience and success of BR AC traction led to export work. Initially, a DC locomotive with some similarity to the BR class 83 was supplied to Polish Railways in 1962, but it was a logical progression from class 83 and E3100 which was to be British industry's first large post-war AC locomotive export order.

This was the Pakistan Western Railway (PWR) scheme to electrify the Khanewal-Lahore line. The decision followed a report produced by the United Kingdom Railway Advisory Service (UKRAS) submitted in 1965, covering a complete electrification project which provided everything required.

The locomotive side of the contract was for 29 5ft 6in gauge Bo-Bo units supplied by a special part of the British Consortium for the Electrification of Pakistan Railways, calling itself the British Rail Traction Group (BRTG). BRTG consisted of the traction divisions of EE and AEI which designed the locomotives and supplied the traction equipment. The mechanical parts were sub-contracted to Metropolitan-Cammell Ltd, which erected them at its Washwood Heath works, Birmingham. The 61 bogies were built by Vulcan Foundry during 1968/9; this included three spares.

For the initial PWR scheme of 178 route miles,

the locomotives were required to meet the following demands.

1. Start a trailing load of 2250 tons on a 0.2 percent gradient.
2. Start a trailing load of 1125 tons on a one percent gradient.
3. Haul a 650-ton passenger train at a balancing speed of 75mph.
4. Haul a 1125-ton freight train at up to 40mph on the Lahore-Rawalpindi section extension, proposed as part two of PWR electrification.

On the second stage, rheostatic braking was needed and the locomotives were built with this in mind, although it was not fitted.

Climatic variations were very different from those in the UK, and included severe sand and dust conditions which necessitated careful insulation techniques; and ambient temperatures of up to 48°C, with relative humidities of 100 percent were also to be expected. The locomotives are able to work over the range from 16.5 to 27.5kV.

The mechanical design of the PWR locomotives is nothing unusual, the superstructure being a load-bearing unit based on main longitudinals and cross-stretchers, the latter providing support for equipment and bogie pivots. The top of the frame is covered in steel sheet. The body comprises a steel frame with welded-on steel panels. The roof of steel is in sections removable for maintenance. Aluminium walkway plates cover cable ducts.

The bogies follow accepted EE practice, being box framed, welded-steel units with rolled-steel side frames, transoms and headstocks. Axlebox design with renewable manganese-steel liners have set bolts for fixing, as in BR practice. SKF roller bearings are fitted. The bogies have a flat centre pivot with renewable liners on the bearing face, and manganese-steel liners on the thrust face; these carry the body. The top half of the pivot is a steel casting spigotted and bolted to the underframe, and the bottom half is integral with the cast-steel swing bolster.

Thyristor control was introduced in this design to control the variation of rectified voltage to the traction motors, the first application to a British AC locomotive, although some EMU sets on BR Eastern and Scottish Regions had thyristor control of their lower power output.

The transformer design is similar to that used in BR class 86, being of semi-core construction with disc-type coils arranged in sandwich formation on the centre limb of the core. Power at 25kV is fed from the overhead wire to the primary of the transformer via a single AEI cross-arm pantograph and air-blast circuit breaker.

The primary rating is 3310 KVA at 22.5kV with forced-oil circulation and air-blast cooling. The secondary winding is in four equal sections. On the secondary terminals are the seven electro-pneumatic tapping contactors. The secondary winding output is taken from the transformer via tapping contactors to the rectifiers. This has 96 silicon diodes and 32 thyristors. The rectifier has the first application of beryllium oxide insulator and heat conductor. It had been used before on BR electric multiple unit trains with naturally-cooled rectifiers.

The traction motors are four-pole series-wound, force-ventilated machines rated at 790hp continuously; they are axle-hung machines with spur gear drive to the wheels. The PWR locomotives are 80-ton units rated continuously at 3160hp at 22.5kV, and a UIC continuous rating of 3650hp at 25kV. They were the first fleet of thyristor-controlled AC locomotives to be exported by any country, and represent a success story for British industry.

The application of thyristors in traction control, with its superior tractive effort characteristics, wheelslip control, plus weight-saving possibilities, at last attracted BR into ordering a thirty-sixth class 87 locomotive to act as a prototype for thyristor equipment. BR has been reticent with thyristor locomotives, possibly because they feared the interference with telecommunications, signalling and the like. Thus the progress of British industry with chopper and thyristor control techniques for UK railways has been limited, although export orders have been executed successfully.

The locomotive was built at Crewe and follows closely the design of the standard class 87, but for recognition it is classified 87/1 and numbered 87101. 87101 is an 87 on the outside, and also very little different inside. At all times it operated as a thyristor locomotive, but it has a second master key hole in the driving master controller by which it can be switched into the 'advanced mode'. This provides for automatic stepless acceleration control. There is a selector switch in the locomotive corridor on No 3 power pack, which brings into circuit a spare set of control panels. The main transformer compartment has no tap changer incorporated.

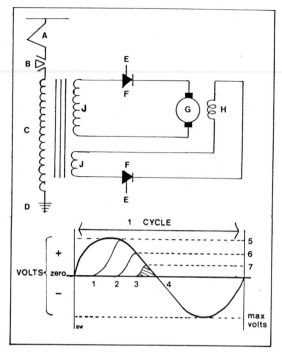

Simplified diagram of a thyristor and its operation.
Upper illustration.

A Pantograph   **B** Air-blast circuit breaker
C Transformer primary winding
D Earth wire via the wheel and rail
E Control gate to thyristor   **F** Thyristor
G Traction motor armature **H** Traction motor field coils
J Transformer secondary winding
Lower illustration
The thyristor in operation; shaded area shows minimum
power, switched-on by the control gate, and switched-off
by the AC cycle reversing   *(Brian Webb)*

A thyristor is a high-speed electrical switch without moving parts. It is a semi-conductor with a special feature which can be used to determine the instant at which conduction starts. Alone or in combination with other thyristors it can switch from little power up to many thousands of kilowatts. More simply, it is a cell or rectifier diode allowing an electric current to be conducted in one direction, but in addition can be switched on fifty or sixty times per second, depending on the application (50Hz/60Hz). Advancing or delaying the time it is switched on varies the average voltage supplied. At the zero volts line in the cycle the thyristor carries no power. However, it cannot be 'switched off' in the accepted meaning; it only stops passing current when the zero voltage point in the cycle is reached and remains 'off' or non-conducting until being switched on.

87101 has its traction motor field coils supplied separately from the supply to the armature, enabling a much finer control at much higher voltage; the field coil can be weakened or strengthened to control wheelslip. With thyristors an extremely smooth stepless control of the transformer output is obtained, being a logical development of the transductor system used in class 83 E3100 and the Pakistan Western thyristor locomotives.

87101 was designed and built to evaluate tractive effort performance (which was superior to class 87 with its normal tap changer control) plus investigations into general electrical engineering considerations, such as power factors, interference due to induced harmonics, as well as effects on electrical supplies and signalling equipment. It also gave British industry a full-size home testbed for development work with high-power traction in addition to that gained with multiple-unit trains of low power.

Important weight saving advantages can be gained by using thyristors in locomotives, which allow elimination of some equipment, and re-design and lightening of the weight in others. Compared with the standard class 87, 87101 did not have an HT tap changer, nor its 25kV auto-transformer. Its transformer weighs only 6 tons, a 5-ton reduction from standard, including the integral oil-pumping equipment radiator and oil conservator. Further weight savings are possible, but 87101 has to be interchangeable with class 87 for normal duties, so deliberate weight-saving in other areas was avoided. Thyristors offer reduced maintenance, simpler transformers, and greater hauling availability (no tractive effort troughs).

In 87101 each motor armature circuit receives current from two rectifier bridges in series, the bridges being composed of two thyristor arms, each with four devices in parallel, and two diode arms, also with four devices in parallel. There are eight thyristors and eight diodes in each bridge, 16 thyristors and 16 diodes per motor armature circuit, giving a total of 64 thyristors and 64 diodes for all armature circuits. This compares with 64 diodes plus tap changer for the class 87, and (more interesting) 576 silicon cells in E3100. Such was the progress in semi-conductors in ten to twelve years. Each motor field is supplied through a bridge with two thyristor arms with single devices and two diode arms with single devices, giving a total of eight thyristors and eight diodes for all field circuits.

The rectifier cases are arranged so that all devices associated with any one motor field/armature circuits are together, and each case contained 18 thyristors and 18 diodes. To eliminate spurious pick-up, some items in the thyristor gate circuits, ie the firing transformers, are placed in close proximity to the thyristors. Elimination of interference in the electronic circuitry has received special attention.

The GECT type G412BZ DC traction motors are generally similar to those used on class 87, but on 87101 these four-pole machines have their main field windings designed to take up to five times the voltage and one-fifth of the current of the series motors to suit separate excitation. The power circuit has four separately fed traction motor armatures and individually controlled field windings. The latter are fed from an auxiliary winding in the main transformer and each goes through a half-thyristor bridge and reversing contacts.

The armature circuit of each motor is supplied from two series-connected half-thyristor bridges, each of which is connected to a separate secondary winding in the main transformer. Two motor armature-bridge circuits share a common secondary winding. Each armature circuit comprises a contactor, overload smoothing-reactor, a dynamic brake resistor and contactor. Also included is a current-measuring unit for monitoring purposes to aid in control.

During operation, the voltage applied to each armature depends on the firing angle of the thyristors in the armature bridges, ie the point in the cycle at which switch 'on' occurs. The resulting current is measured, and a derivative controls the value of the current admitted to the field, so that the current in the armature is compared to field strength and is appropriate to the conditions required. Motor voltage is built up stage by stage, so that at half voltage one bridge per motor is used, and the firing of that bridge's thyristors is advanced until free-firing is obtained. The fully-retarded thyristors in the second bridge are then gradually advanced, giving an increasing voltage from the secondary winding. When both bridges are fully advanced full motor voltage is attained. To increase speed further, the thyristors controlling the field are retarded and the resulting increase in the proportion of armature to field current gives weak field running.

Immediate suppression of wheelslip is carried out by the built in 'shunt' arrangement of the separately excited traction motors. In persistent slipping conditions affecting only some wheels, the differing speeds of the motors is determined automatically by speed probes on the axle gearwheels, and the strength of the field of the slipping motors is set against the strongest field, the armature current reducing until wheelslip is corrected. If all axles are slipping, the acceleration is detached and the fields are clamped; the armature current reduction is speeded by phase delay of the thyristor until slipping stops.

During dynamic braking each armature is connected to its braking resistor and the field current increased by thyristor control until a train retardation similar to that which would be given by the air brakes is reached. An overriding current limit is fitted to control this. When the controller is moved to 'off', the thyristors are used to relieve the motor contactors of normal rupturing duty. They are also used to provide rapid protection in the event of flashovers.

The controls of 87101 are standardised to BR AC locomotive requirements, but an additional scale of handle position markings for setting the tractive effort (TE) is fitted. This is used for advanced driving and for this the required speed is also set by a control.

A tractive effort boost button allows an increase for short periods. That selected demonstrates higher adhesion levels and remains constant until the set speed is attained or until maximum voltage is reached.

87101 has in practice shown some 19 percent greater hauling ability than a standard class 87 locomotive, this being due to its thyristor control, separately-excited traction motors, with better slip characteristics than series motors. In the former there are no troughs in performance since no tap changing is involved, and in the latter case each individual traction motor corrects itself at wheelslip. The control of 87101 helps weight transfer, each axle's loading being taken into account, so that the tractive effort in each motor at times of weight transfer (starting and stopping) is adjusted to suit its weight loading.

In spite of much caution at the introduction of 87101 onto BR, which hampered operation in the advanced mode, the interference that it was feared would upset power supply, telecommunications, and signalling, has been proved to be minimal. Indeed, the adverse interference effects arising from trials of 87101 were also found on standard AC locomotives!

87101 causes some interference to signalling, especially if a particular signalbox happens to be taking its power supply from the overhead wire rather than from the mains supply. Under these conditions, as 87101 stops taking power from the overhead wire, a rapid surge in the overhead wire voltage upsets the highly-sensitive protection equipment associated with the power supply to the signalbox. The protection equipment detects rate of rise of voltage, and it was thought that the voltage regulation of the signalbox supply required equipment which reacted as quickly as that on 87101 with its rapidly switching thyristors.

So far as telecommunications circuits are concerned, better screening over telephone cables, or moving cables further away from the overhead wire, has largely cut out problems of noise on the telephone lines. Extended tests with APT power car SC49001 parked on a siding at Tebay with all equipment on, full load against the hydro-kinetic brake, with drive shafts uncoupled, and with 87101 running past, have provided much useful data on these interference problems, so often the source of reservations about the use of thyristor control. Without doubt, 87101 is the best AC electric locomotive on BR.

Commencing in 1977, GECT began delivery of a fleet of 20 lightweight 25kV AC Bo-Bo electric locomotives to the Taiwan Railway Administration (TRA). This was the second British export order for thyristor-controlled locomotives. The locomotives form part of a very comprehensive scheme for TRA, involving GEC Transportation Projects Ltd, and including other British suppliers engaged in up-grading the permanent way, telecommunications, power supply and distribution etc. GECT not only supplied the locomotives, but also 13 five-car luxury electric multiple-unit train sets with thyristor control, built in 1977/8 by BREL at York.

TRA is of 3ft 6in gauge and the GECT motive power is operating on the Kee-Lung-Kao-Hsiung line. The route involves hilly mountain sections and flat coastal lines. On the former, the locomotives are hauling singly loads of up to 1250 tons, and in multiple up to 2000 tons, limitations being imposed by the drawbar. On the mountain grades a 2.5 percent grade rules; passenger trains of up to 525 tons may be taken over the mountain lines by one locomotive. Temperatures with the locomotives' operating range are 0-40°C; altitudes vary between 30 and 400 metres, and snow is found in winter on the mountain section.

Mechanically, the locomotives are conventional, based on a superstructure with an underframe of main longitudinal side members, interconnected by cross-members at equipment and bogie pivot mounting points, also at the drag boxes and bufferbeams. A simple steel body frame clad with welded-on steel panels is used, and the roof is wholly removable between the cabs, including the twin pantographs. The body forms a load-bearing structure.

The bogies are welded from steel plate into box-frame units, and the axleboxes have SKF bearings. The bogies carry the body on flat centre pivots, the top half of the pivot casting being spigotted and bolted to the underframe, while the bottom half is integral with the fabricated-steel swing bolster. The swing links and coil secondary springs are outside the bogie frame, lateral loading of the secondary being eliminated by anchoring the spring seats to the swing bolster by long arms with pin joints. A spring control unit links both bogies to give interaction on curves to reduce flange and rail wear.

The locomotives' mechanical parts were designed by GECT in the UK, but erection was sub-contracted to the Union Carriage & Wagon Co Ltd (UCW) of South Africa, a firm with a long association of electric traction with GECT and its constituent companies. The locomotives are TRA numbers E101-E120.

The equipment in the TRA locomotives owes much to the work put in on 87101. The use of thyristor control in these lightweight 70-ton locomotives allows full use of available adhesion. The smooth, notchless control of tractive effort enables working at the peak of the notches, which would be associated with a non-thyristor tap changer type of locomotive.

The traction motors are adapted from the AEI 283 AY motor, of which some 3000 are in service on South African Railways in class 6E1 3000V DC locomotives. In its modified form, it is GECT model G413AZ, a DC separately-excited, non-compensated, four-pole machine with a continuous rating of 1470V, 380A, 660rpm, 530kW, the 283 AY motor being of series type. It is an axle-hung, nose-suspended unit.

Two GEC cross-arm pantographs are fitted on each locomotive, and the vacuum circuit-breakers are similar to the type fitted to some class 87 locomotives of BR. Compared with the PWR locomotives, the TRA locomotives have a much simpler arrangement.

The possibility that 50kV instead of 25kV AC electrification may become a future mode for some overseas railway electrification schemes is significant because it is British expertise which has secured the first foothold in this field.

GECT, with traction equipment from its own and constituent companies at work on all the world's standard DC and AC systems, is unrivalled in its achievement by its involvement in the world's first commercial 50kV system.

Some work in the USA has been undertaken; US-General Electric has a six-kilometre test track. The US government has an 18½-mile test track at its Pueblo research centre, and there is the 77-mile Black Mesa & Lake Powell Railroad in Arizona. This is doing commercial haulage, but is still an experimental line.

Nevertheless, these are entirely eclipsed by GECT involvement in South Africa in the 536-mile Sishen-Saldanha iron-ore line, electrified at 50kV to avoid drastic power drop in the centre portions of the route, devoid of feeder stations, where the voltage in the overhead wire is much less than 50kV. For this reason the locomotives will operate throughout the 25kV-55kV range. This line is single-track, passing through much semi-desert country subject to severe dust and electrical storms, and on coastal sections with Atlantic salt-laden air and sea mists.

The locomotives being supplied by GECT incorporate traction equipment from the UK, and although the locomotives were designed by GECT, like the TRA locomotives, the mechanical parts were made and the locomotives erected by UCW, as sub-contractors in South Africa.

A total of 25 Co-Co 3ft 6in gauge thyristor-controlled locomotives were delivered, the first being in service in 1978. They are SAR class 9E and will operate three in multiple on 20,000-ton ore trains of 202 bogie wagons.

The locomotives are somewhat unusual single-cab units with full-width bodies, which are lowered at the rear to accommodate pantographs and associated rooftop gear, and provide sufficient clearance for the 50kV overhead wire. Such an arrangement would not be tolerated on BR, but on the line where the 9E class operate there are no station platforms so the danger of the 50kV is not so pronounced.

The mechanical design is again conventional. The underframe is based on two very conspicuous longitudinal side members connected by cross-members for bogie and equipment mounting, and at the ends for drag boxes and bufferbeams. A steel body frame covered with steel panels welded-on is used, the roof being fitted with removable sections for maintenance access. The whole body is an integral load-bearing structure.

Fabricated steel bogies with Timken roller-bearing axleboxes are fitted. Coil springs support the bogie frame on equalising beams. Body bogie pivot arrangements are similar to the TRA locomotives. The fabricated steel bolster is supported on rubber units and located by traction brackets on top of the bogie frame. A container is placed under the locomotive for housing a small motorcycle used by the crew for train inspection purposes!

The 9E class power equipment has much in common with BR 87101 and the TRA locomotives, the policy of GECT being to use where possible tried and tested equipment, or to adapt such equipment rather than develop new items. This is obviously advantageous in cost and spares, but of course traction development work continues in the search for better methods.

One departure is the provision of a motor-alternator set in each locomotive so that a constant voltage output is achieved for feeding the locomotive's auxiliary equipment, motors, etc, no matter whether the locomotive is taking power at any range within the 25-55kV band.

The traction motors of type GEC G415AZ are modified and up-rated versions of the 283 AY motor, demonstrating again the trend of modification of trusted components as part of GEC policy. They are axle-hung, four-pole machines with forced ventilation and, in this case, separate excitation. Drive is through solid resilient spur gears. Dynamic braking is fitted, and all locomotives are air-braked, but six have in addition vacuum-brake gear for working trains so fitted.

Although the locomotives and line are now South African Railways' property, the original order was placed by the South African Iron & Steel Industrial Corporation (ISCOR). The 168-ton locomotives are the world's most powerful 3ft 6in gauge electric locomotives, having a starting tractive effort of over 121,000lb at 33 percent adhesion.

Trends in BR AC traction involve the suburban electrification out of King's Cross and St Pancras, the former being in use, and both systems using EMU sets. So far as main lines are concerned, the

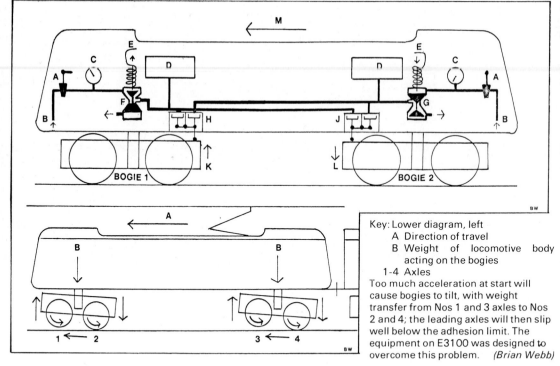

Key: Lower diagram, left
   A Direction of travel
   B Weight of locomotive body acting on the bogies
   1-4 Axles
Too much acceleration at start will cause bogies to tilt, with weight transfer from Nos 1 and 3 axles to Nos 2 and 4; the leading axles will then slip well below the adhesion limit. The equipment on E3100 was designed to overcome this problem.   *(Brian Webb)*

Simplified diagram showing the weight transfer equipment fitted to E3100.
Key: Upper diagram
   A Air pressure regulating valve (left hand one open)
   B Air supply
   C Pressure gauge (left hand one registering)
   D Volume reservoir
   E Electric supply
   F Electro-pneumatic valve energised and open
   G Electro-pneumatic valve de-energised, closed and vented to atmosphere
   H Operating pistons
   K Direction of bogie movement upwards
   L Direction of bogie movement downwards
   M Direction of locomotive travel

When the driver selects forward position, and opens the power handle to notch/run-up, switches on the traction motor contactors allow control current of 110V DC to energise the coil of electro magnet (F). This pulls up the valve and seals the lower exhaust valve. Air passes through the open upper valve on cylinder (H) at the inner end of No 1 bogie, allowing it to lift at its rear end. Air passes to cylinder (J) also, on the inner end of No 2 bogie, causing it to lower at its leading end. Normal weight transfer is thus compensated and bogie tilting overcome when starting a train from rest.

three prototype Advanced Passenger Trains (APT) were to be introduced in stages during 1979. Depending on the success of APT, future Inter-City trains will be of this type, there being a definite drift away from locomotive-hauled trains so far as passenger traffic is concerned. There are two schools of thought, and some continue to uphold the locomotive powered push-and-pull system. The introduction of class 47 2580hp diesel-electric, and the possibility of using class 81 AC locomotives, in Scotland, and on the Eastern Region GE section respectively, are pointers to this.

Future AC locomotive policy is expected to be the introduction of a freight locomotive, most probably a Co-Co, due to the inherent disadvantages of high horsepower to low adhesion, typified by the latest Bo-Bo locomotives. In class 87 5000hp in 81 tons 19cwt adhesive weight gives problems when employed on 1400-ton Freightliners over Shap and Beattock. All trains over 700 tons have to be double-headed, either in multiple with one locomotive crew, or in tandem with two locomotive crews, a waste of motive power and labour resources. This is in contrast with the 21-year-old class 40 1Co-Co1 diesel-electric locomotives regularly hauling over 1000 tons

Above: The first BR thyristor-controlled locomotive was 87101, built at Crewe in 1975. This derivative of class 87 has undergone and still undergoes testing work in connection with future AC locomotives required for BR. Here 87101 is seen on test in 1975, before being named *Stephenson.* *(British Rail)*

Below: The world's first commercial 50kV AC electrification is in South Africa where a 536 mile iron-ore line between Sishen and Saldanha is being operated by a fleet of British-designed and equipped Co-Co locomotives. GEC Traction, using UCW as sub-contractors for the locomotive mechanical parts, is supplying 25 locomotives which will operate on loads of up to 20,000 tons, three locomotives in multiple. *(GEC Traction)*

COMPARATIVE DIMENSIONS AND EQUIPMENT VARIATIONS FOR AC LOCOMOTIVE CLASSES 86 and 87

Locomotive classification	AL6	86/0	AL6	86/0	AL6	86/1
Power equipment supplier	EE and AEI		EE and AEI		EE and AEI	
and locomotive builder	BR and VF		BR and VF		BR and VF	
BR Diagram No in 1978	86 bX		86 cX		86 laX	
Original Loco No Series	E3101 - E3200 Series		E3101 - E3200 Series		E3143/50/91	
Current Loco No Series	86001 - 39		86001 - 39		86101 - 3	
Weight in working order	81T 10C		82T 11C		85T 8C	
Length over buffers	58′ 6″		58′ 6″		58′ 6″	
Max. height with pan. down	13′ 9/16″		13′ 9/16″		13′ 9/16″	
Width over body	8′ 8¼″		8′ 8¼″		8′ 8¼″	
Bogie wheelbase	10′ 9″		10′ 9″		10′ 9 1/8″	
Bogie centres	32′ 9″		32′ 9″		32′ 9″	
Total wheelbase	43′ 6″		43′ 6″		43′ 6″	
Wheel diameter	3′ 9″		3′ 9″		3′ 9½″	
Bogie type	fabricated steel		fabricated steel		fabricated steel	
	Alsthom suspension		Alsthom suspension		Flexicoil suspension	
Pantograph type	Stone-Faiveley and AEI		Stone-Faiveley and AEI		Stone-Faiveley	
Main circuit breaker type	Brown-Boveri		Brown-Boveri		Brown-Boveri	
Main rectifier	Silicon semi-conductor		Silicon semi-conductor		Silicon semi-conductor	
Main transformer	oil cooled		oil cooled		oil cooled	
	HT tap changing		HT tap changing		HT tap changing	
Traction motor type	AEI 282 AZ 4 poles		AEI 282 AZ 4 poles		GEC G412 AZ 4 poles	
Traction motor suspension	axle hung nose suspension		axle hung nose suspension		frame mounted	
Traction motor drive type	single reduction gear		single reduction gear		ASEA shaft	
Gear ratio	22:65		22:65		32:73	
Traction motor cooling	1 blower per motor		1 blower per motor		1 blower per motor	
Maximum tractive effort	58000 lbs		58000 lbs		58000 lbs	
Continuous tractive effort						
on weakest field/mph	20,000 lbs 67 mph		20,000 lbs 67 mph		21,300 lbs 87 mph	
Maximum rail H.P./mph	5900 HP 38 mph		5900 HP 38 mph		5000 HP 87 mph	
Speeds maximum mph	100		100		100	
Brake equipment make	Westinghouse		Westinghouse		Westinghouse	
Main air compressor make	Westinghouse		Westinghouse		Westinghouse	
Exhauster make	Reavell		Reavell		Reavell	

unaided over Ais Gill on the Settle-Carlisle line. There has been much talk about the future six-axle AC locomotive design, for which there are three basic choices: 1.—The conventional Co-Co with six axle-hung traction motors, probably limited to 80-100mph. 2.—The mono-motor bogied Co-Co with one traction motor on each bogie, adaptable to 80mph freight or 125mph passenger work by changing gear ratios. 3.—A Bo-Bo-Bo locomotive using three existing bogies, say of the type used on class 87. It would seem that the Co-Co type with individual axle driving motors would have the greatest appeal for BR, which has experience with this form of layout in diesel-electric locomotives, axle-hung motors being used. The disadvantages of individual axle wheelslip would be controlled by thyristors. Standard motors of an existing design could be used, and in the event of a motor failing, such an arrangement would permit the locomotive to complete its work on five motors.

If BR reverts to a policy of running passenger trains with AC locomotives, a Co-Co mono-motor bogie type could be the solution. The large motor would be bogie-mounted, as on the SNCF locomotives, and protrude upwards into the locomotive body. The method is to mount two motors on one shaft transversely across the locomotive body, gearing between the two motors driving to each of the three axles, and then by Alsthom flexible quill drive to each wheel, the gear ratio being changed to suit operational requirements. This type offers certain advantages, all axles being coupled together on each bogie, making wheelslip no great problem; larger traction motors can be used as they are not restricted by the size of the bogie frame, as with axle-hung or individual bogie-mounted motors; improved insulation and larger conductors can be fitted in the motors to handle heavier current; the bogie can be made with a shorter wheel-base than a Co bogie, giving a three-axle C bogie no larger in this respect than the current BR Bo bogie on

AL6	86/2	AL6	86/2	87 + 87/1		NOTES
EE and AEI		EE and AEI		GECT		
BR and VF		BR and VF		BR		
86 2bX		86 2cX		87 aA and 87 1aA		
E3101 - E3200 Series		E3101 - E3200 Series		87001 - 35	87101	
86204 - 61		86204 - 61		87001 - 35	87101	
83T 13C		84T 11C		81T 19C	77T 17C	
58'6"		58'6"		58'6"		
13' 9/16"		13' 9/16"		13' 1¼"		
8'8¼"		8'8¼"		8'8¼"		
10'9 1/8"		10'9 1/8"		10'9 1/8"		
32'9"		32'9"		32'9"		
43'6"		43'6"		43'6 1/8"		
3'9½"		3'9½"		3'9½"		
fabricated steel		fabricated steel		fabricated steel		
Flexicoil suspension		Flexicoil suspension		Flexicoil suspension		
Stone-Faiveley and AEI		Stone-Faiveley and AEI		GEC		
Brown-Boveri		Brown-Boveri		GEC		
Silicon semi-conductor		Silicon semi-conductor		Silicon semi-conductor		
oil cooled		oil cooled		oil cooled oil cooled		
HT tap changing		HT tap changing		HT tap changing Thyristor		
AEI 282 BZ 4 poles		AEI 282 BZ 4 poles		GEC G412 AZ 4 poles		87101 has separately excited
axle hung nose suspension		axle hung nose suspension		frame mounted		traction motors type G412 BZ
single reduction gear		single reduction gear		ASEA shaft		
22:65		22:65		32:73		
1 blower per motor		1 blower per motor		1 blower per motor		
46500 lbs		46500 lbs		58000 lbs		
19200 lbs 77½ mph		19200 lbs 77½ mph		21300 lbs	21600 lbs	
				87 mph	84 mph	
6100 HP at 49½ mph		6100 HP at 49½ mph		5000 HP 87 mph	4850 HP 84 mph	
100		100		100		
Westinghouse		Westinghouse		Westinghouse		
Westinghouse		Westinghouse		Westinghouse		
Reavell		Reavell		not fitted		

classes 86 and 87, enabling similar-radius curves to be negotiated. This concept is largely favoured in France but its final drive gearbox complications are a big disadvantage.

The Bo-Bo-Bo design has advantages on sharp curves; it uses a standard bogie and motors, thus saving design costs and easing spares supplies. The loading and unloading of the centre bogie, with the rigid locomotive body raising or lowering in the centre when track gradients fluctuate, can be overcome by suspension design as it has in Switzerland where gradient changes and curves are often more severe than those on BR. On curves, the centre of the necessarily longer Bo-Bo-Bo locomotive moves a greater distance laterally in relation to the track. The Bo-Bo-Bo layout would be useful should future electrification be decided for, possibly, the lines into northern Scotland, where sharp curves abound.

Without doubt, much further main line electrification for BR is 'on the cards'. The mid-1978 plans for electrification prepared by BR and submitted for study by a joint BR and Department of Transport committee could well see a massive expansion of the BR AC locomotive fleet from the present 224 (originally 236) to between 1000 and 1200. In whatever form they appear they would be needed mainly for freight traffic. The most comprehensive programme under scrutiny would involve almost 70 percent of BR freight being electrically-hauled; the present proportion is about 15 percent. It is possible therefore that if the largest plan is approved, 50 to 60 AC locomotives a year would be built for BR over a period of two decades, coupled with a certain amount of new diesel-electric traction (and successful development for battery traction work of the sodium-sulphur battery). This would represent some sizeable contracts for the British rail traction industry, British Rail Engineering Ltd and, one hopes, the British locomotive builders.

INDEX

An impression of what a possible Bo-Bo-Bo AC locomotive could have looked like for BR. As it is, it is likely that class 89 will be a Co-Co design. *(Brian Webb)*

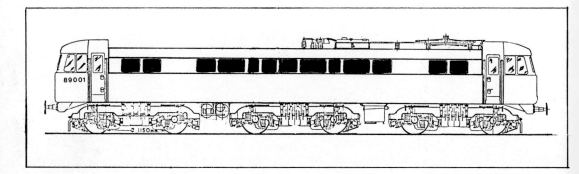